Another Day,
Another $11,247.63

Another Day, Another $11,247.63

by Jeff Millar and Bill Hinds

Andrews and McMeel, Inc.
A Universal Press Syndicate Company
Kansas City • New York

A Tank McNamara Collection

ISBN: 0-8362-2016-1

Library of Congress Catalog Card Number: 82-74420

First Printing, March 1983
Second Printing, May 1983

*T*his anthology is a scrapbook of snapshots assembled not in chronological order but by categories. You put together all the pictures of the kid at the beach. All the pictures of the kid in his Halloween costumes. From one Fotomat print to the next, the kid's going to get bigger and smaller, his hair's going to get shorter and longer.

There have been changes in Tank over the period from which these snapshots were taken. Some were deliberate, some were utterly unconscious. They will leap out at you when one snapshot is juxtaposed with one taken two years before or after. One wouldn't have noticed most of them — I didn't until I put this together — when Tank is consumed one bite at a time, twenty-four hours between bites.

The corridors of the Universal Press Syndicate headquarters are enlivened with poster-sized gag photographs of UPS creators. Garry Trudeau chose to pose in elegant, ice-cream-white top hat and tails. Abigail Van Buren peeks from behind a rose. Cathy Guisewite luxuriates on a sofa wearing not-so-impressive sweatshirt and jeans. Pat Oliphant, freed from social and political commentary, spirits along on a mini-bike.

The photograph of the Tank McNamara team is of me praying, Bill drawing, and a man from Federal Express pointing to his wristwatch. The corridors of UPS surely ring with sardonic chuckles. Not even Federal can help when it absolutely, positively had to have been there yesterday.

Topical humor has the shelf life of iceberg lettuce and the same buyer appeal when it hits a newspaper reader's lap wilted. Hypertension spread along the supply chain is the price of getting the commodity to market when it's still crisp.

You can't see them, but pasted with gratitude into this album of snapshots is everybody at UPS and all the editors at our client newspapers who've ever crunched into a Gelusil tablet and thought of Millar/Hinds.

— **Jeff Millar**

...AND NOW ARLENE AND I WANT TO WELCOME TO THE BIGEYECENTER NEWS TEAM OUR NEW SPORTSCASTER, JACK SNIFFER...

FOLKS, I'M PUTTING ON THIS BLACK ARMBAND, AND I'M NOT TAKING IT OFF UNTIL SOMEBODY... I DON'T CARE IF IT'S THE PRESIDENT, THE POPE... UNTIL **SOMEBODY** CAN ASSURE ME THAT AMERICA WILL HAVE PRO FOOTBALL THIS YEAR...

THE PRO SPORTS AGENTS ASSN. IS OPPOSED TO THE PRO FOOTBALL UNION'S CONTRACT PROPOSALS.

THE ISSUE IS VERY COMPLICATED, TANK, BUT AT THE BOTTOM LINE, THERE IS THE ALARMING POSSIBILITY THAT IF THE AGREEMENT WERE SIGNED, SPORTS AGENTS COULD IN FACT HAVE TO START WORKING FOR A LIVING.

THE PLAYERS' UNION PROPOSAL WOULD ALL BUT ELIMINATE THE ROLE OF THE PLAYER'S AGENT IN PRO FOOTBALL.

BOTH PLAYERS AND OWNERS SHOULD BE AWARE OF THE SPORTS AGENTS' IMPORTANT FUNCTION.

SPORTS AGENTS' ASSN. SPOKESMAN

WE'VE SELFLESSLY TAKEN ALL THE HEAT FOR THE INSANE JUMP IN PLAYER SALARIES.

THINK, FOLKS: WHOM WOULD **YOU** RATHER PERCEIVE AS OBSCENELY GREEDY? THAT QUARTERBACK YOU IDOLIZE OR HIS AGENT?

WE MUST CONVINCE OUR CLIENTS THAT THE PLAYERS UNION'S COMPLICATED COMPENSATION PLAN IS NOT IN THEIR BEST INTERESTS.

SPORTS AGENTS ASSN.

OUR CLIENTS TEND TO BE YOUNG, IN MOST CASES UNDEREDUCATED AND ALMOST ALWAYS FINANCIALLY UNSOPHISTICATED.

TAKE ADVANTAGE OF IT.

THAT %⊙*&*! UNION'S PUSHING US OUT FROM UNDER THE MONEY TREE, GUYS!

MILLAR/HINDS

HEY, IF THE UNION SAYS WE SHARE THE BOX OFFICE PIE, THAT'S GOOD ENOUGH FOR ME.

BUCK, I'M YOUR AGENT AND YOUR FRIEND. I UNDERSTAND.

HEY, IF IT COMES DOWN TO CHOOSING BETWEEN MY UNION AND MY AGENT...THE ISSUE HERE IS SOLIDARITY, RIGHT?

BUCK, SOLIDARITY WILL RUN YOU $72,789.65 A YEAR.

SAY WHAT?!?

NOW, UNDER THE PRO AGENT ASSN.'S 'I GOT MINE, JACK' PLAN....

MILLAR/HINDS

GOOD NEWS! BUCK BAKER'S SOLIDARITY WITH THE PLAYERS' UNION MIGHT BE WEAKENING.

QUARTERBACKS ARE THE FIRST TO FINK...

SPORTS AGENTS' ASSN.

SURE. FOR HOD CARRIERS OR STEELWORKERS, UNIONS MAKE SENSE.

AND EVEN FOR FOOTBALL PLAYERS AT THE UNSKILLED POSITIONS.

BUT FOR AN NFL SUPERSTAR QUARTERBACK?

BUCK BAKER? CARRYING A LUNCH BUCKET?

TACKY, BUCK.

TACKY.

MILLAR/HINDS

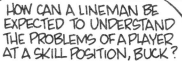

BUCK, LOOK AT WHO'S PRESIDENT OF THE PLAYERS' UNION...

HE'S A GUARD, BUCK. A LINEMAN.

HOW CAN A LINEMAN BE EXPECTED TO UNDERSTAND THE PROBLEMS OF A PLAYER AT A SKILL POSITION, BUCK?

TAKE THE TERRIBLE FRUSTRATION OF HAVING TWICE AS MUCH MONEY THAN YOU KNOW WHAT TO DO WITH.

IS A UNION **REALLY** EQUIPPED TO DEAL WITH THAT, BUCK...?

WHAT ARGUMENT IS THE PLAYERS' UNION USING WITH YOUR DISSIDENT MEMBERS?

TAKE A MAILGRAM TO BUCK BAKER. 'DEAR BUCK, WE'RE LOOKING FORWARD TO PLAYING THE BASHERS THIS SEASON, SO UNION MEMBERS CAN DISCUSS MATTERS OF MUTUAL INTEREST OVER YOUR BROKEN, MANGLED BODY.'

IF IT GETS OUT TO THE MEDIA THAT THE PLAYERS' UNION IS THREATENING DISSIDENTS WITH **VIOLENCE**...

THE MAILGRAM MERELY SAID WE WERE LOOKING FORWARD TO MEETING BUCK BAKER ON THE FIELD THIS SEASON.

'...SO WE CAN INSERT YOUR HEAD INTO THE ASTROTURF UP TO YOUR CHINSTRAP.'

OH, FOR PETE'S SAKE, THAT'S SIMPLY A METAPHOR FOR FRANK AND USEFUL DISCUSSIONS.

SURE, I'M PRO-STRIKE, BUT FIRST OF ALL I'M A BASHER. IF DURING A GAME ANY PLAYERS' UNION GOON FROM ANY OPPONENT TEAM LAYS AN UNNECESSARY FINGER ON BUCK BAKER JUST BECAUSE HE'S AGAINST A STRIKE...

WELL, LET'S JUST SAY THERE ARE SOME GUYS ON OTHER TEAMS WHO'VE SHOT THEIR MOUTH OFF AGAINST THE STRIKE TOO...

ARE YOU FOLLOWING THIS?

SHH. DON'T BREAK MY CONCENTRATION.

ALTHOUGH THE STRIKE THREAT LOOMS, THE BASHERS COACH CONTINUES WITH TRAINING CAMP PLANS...

ON THE SPOT SPORTS

WE'LL HAVE OUR USUAL SCRIMMAGE GAMES, TANK. STARTING OFFENSE VS. STARTING DEFENSE. ROOKIES VS. VETERANS.

PRO-UNION PLAYERS VS. ANTI-UNION PLAYERS, WHICH MIGHT BE **VERY** INTERESTING...

THE LEAGUE SUGGESTS A $100 FINE TO ANY PLAYER WHO PARTICIPATES IN THE UNION'S SYMBOLIC PRE-GAME 'SOLIDARITY HANDSHAKE'--

--BUT I'M GONNA MAKE THE FINE A WEEK'S SALARY!

WHAT'S MORE IMPORTANT? UNION BROTHERHOOD? OR A FEW DOLLARS?

UHHH... HOW MUCH IF I JUST WAVE FROM THE SIDELINES?

COACH

Panel 1: SURE, I BELIEVE IN UNION SOLIDARITY. BUT TO GET FINED A WEEK'S SALARY JUST FOR A SYMBOLIC HANDSHAKE WITH THE OTHER TEAM...

Panel 2: HOW ABOUT WE BRIBE SOMEBODY TO TURN OUT THE LIGHTS, RUN OUT TO MIDFIELD, SHAKE HANDS, THEN RUN BACK BEFORE ANYBODY...

Panel 3: WE WOULD KNOW, GUYS. WE WOULD KNOW WE DID IT...

Panel 4: GEE, I SEEMED TO HAVE PULLED SOMETHING DURING WARM-UPS. BUT I'LL MAKE A SYMBOLIC GESTURE HERE FROM THE BENCH TO SHOW MY UNION BROTHERHOOD.

Panel 5: THE PLAYERS HAVE MADE THEIR INDIVIDUAL CHOICES BETWEEN A SYMBOLIC MIDFIELD HANDSHAKE AND A STIFF FINE...

Panel 6: WAS THE SYMBOLIC GESTURE WHERE YOU POLISHED THE CLASP ON COACH'S CLIPBOARD?

THE SARCASM WAS THAT OBVIOUS, HUH?

Panel 7: TANK, BOTH TEAM'S PREGAME 'SOLIDARITY HANDSHAKE' WAS A SHABBY STUNT TO MAKE THE PUBLIC THINK THESE $65,000-A-YEAR ENTERTAINERS HAVE SOMETHING IN COMMON WITH A FACTORY WORKER WHO GETS $9.83 AN HOUR -- WHEN HE'S NOT LAID OFF.

Panel 8: ANYBODY WITH ANY SENSITIVITY WILL REALIZE THAT THIS HAS AS MUCH TO DO WITH THE REAL AMERICAN LABOR MOVEMENT'S STRUGGLE AS --

Panel 9: FOLKS, I'M PUTTING ON MY JOHN WAYNE HAT, BECAUSE THE DUKE WOULD HAVE BEEN PROUD OF THESE TRUE AMERICANS. I DON'T MIND TELLING YOU THAT HANDSHAKE GOT ME A LIT-TLE CHOKED UP...

JACK SNIFFER
BIGEYE CENTER SPORTS

OUR RANK AND FILE UNION BROTHERS AND SISTERS MAKING $10 AN HOUR DON'T IDENTIFY WITH US...

PLAYERS' UNION
MEMBERS ONLY

...SO EVERYBODY TAKES ONE OF THESE ON THE FIELD.

SCUFF 'EM UP A LITTLE, GUYS, MAKE 'EM LOOK USED....

LUNCH PAILS

MILLAR/HINDS

THE PLAYERS REALIZE THAT SOME OF OUR UNION BROTHERS AND SISTERS DON'T SUPPORT OUR STRUGGLE FOR A LIVING WAGE...

...AND FRANKLY, TANK, WE'RE A LITTLE HURT. SURE, WE MAKE A COUPLE OF HUNDRED THOUSAND MORE A YEAR THAN THE AVERAGE WORKER, BUT...

MILLAR/HINDS

HEY, PEOPLE, THIS IS A HARD HAT TOO...

AFL-CIO

TANK, THE PLAYERS ARE EXPECTING OUR UNION BROTHERS AND SISTERS TO SUPPORT US.

SOLIDARITY FOREVER!

12

$9,234.23/HOUR

MILLAR/HINDS

BLEEP SOLIDARITY.

$9.23/HOUR

YES, THE ENTIRE NFL SEASON IS IN DANGER, BUT THERE'S STILL HOPE FOR PRO FOOTBALL.

THERE IS?

THERE'S THE CHANCE THE PLAYERS' UNION ALL-STAR GAMES COULD RESUME.

PEOPLE NEED TO FEEL THAT THEIR TIME IS WORTH SOMETHING. THE INACTIVITY CAUSED BY A STRIKE CHALLENGES ONE'S SENSE OF SELF-ESTEEM.

IMAGINE, TANK, THE SHOCK OF REALIZING THAT YOU ACTUALLY WATCHED SUMO WRESTLING...

...AND THEN SUDDENLY TRASH SPORTS WASN'T GOOD ENOUGH FOR NETWORK TV. BUT ONCE THEIR PRECIOUS PRO FOOTBALL WAS GONE, THEY WEREN'T SO PROUD.

GENTLEMEN, STARRRRRT YOURRRRRR REEEEFRIGERATORS!

JOE KRAMDEN WAS KICKED OFF THE TEAM WHEN HE REFUSED TO OBEY HIS COACH'S ORDER TO LEAVE THE BENCH TO FIGHT.

AN OUTCAST IN THE NHL, HE HAD TO START BACK AT THE BOTTOM OF HOCKEY'S MINOR LEAGUES.

BUT WITH FISTS, STICKS, FOLDING CHAIRS AND BROKEN BEER BOTTLES WHEN HE COULD FIND 'EM, HE GOT BACK TO THE BIG LEAGUES.

TUESDAY AT 9, 8 CENTRAL, THE MADE-FOR-TV MOVIE OF THE YEAR: "FIGHTING BACK: THE JOE KRAMDEN STORY."

THE WORD'S OUT ON YOU, KRAMDEN. YOU DISOBEYED A DIRECT ORDER.

OKAY, I MADE A MISTAKE. BUT IF NO ONE WILL LET ME PUT ON A UNIFORM, HOW CAN I PROVE I'M WILLING TO FIGHT?

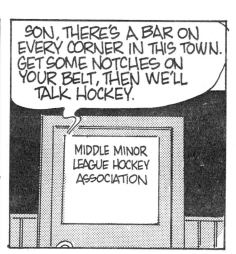

SON, THERE'S A BAR ON EVERY CORNER IN THIS TOWN. GET SOME NOTCHES ON YOUR BELT, THEN WE'LL TALK HOCKEY.

MIDDLE MINOR LEAGUE HOCKEY ASSOCIATION

...THEN I TRIED THE ARMPIT LEAGUE. BUT EVEN IN INSTEP, NORTH DAKOTA, THEY'D HEARD OF THE MAN WHO WAS KICKED OUT OF THE NHL FOR NOT FIGHTING...

BAR

HEY, KRAMDEN, THE YWCA IS DOWN THE STREET, HAR HAR...

WHACK!

SON, I LIKE YOUR STYLE. EVER SEE ONE OF THESE...?

REMEMBER JOE KRAMDEN?

SHUNNED IN THE NHL FOR NOT FIGHTING?

HE'S DOWN IN THE ARMPIT LEAGUE. JUST GOT A 7-HOUR, 45-MINUTE PENALTY FOR CROSS-CHECKING AND CIVIL INSURRECTION.

KEEP AN EYE ON HIM. IT'S A POTENTIAL COMEBACK PLAYER-OF-THE-YEAR STORY.

TANK McNAMARA'S PLAYING HIMSELF IN THIS TV MOVIE...

JOE KRAMDEN, THE PLAYER WHO REFUSED TO FIGHT, IS ABOUT TO WIN HIS WAY BACK INTO THE NATIONAL HOCKEY LEAGUE.

TO SHOW THE NHL I'VE GOT WHAT IT TAKES, I'VE HAD TO PUNCH OUT PLAYERS, REFEREES, SPECTATORS, BUS DRIVERS, WAITERS AND...

...NOTHING PERSONAL, UNDERSTAND.

HEY, ANYTHING TO HELP.

...IT TOOK TWO YEARS, BUT YOU MADE IT BACK TO THE NHL. NOW ALL YOU NEED IS A CHANCE TO SHOW THEM...

JOE, I NEED A MAN TO LEAVE THE BENCH AND GET INTO THAT FIGHT.

I'M YOUR MAN, COACH.

...AND THIS CROWD OPENS ITS HEART! IT'S A STANDING-O FOR JOE KRAMDEN!!

CLAP! CLAP!

TANK, SHE DIDN'T DO AS WELL AS EVERYBODY EXPECTED, AND SHE'LL BE OUT OF THE GOLD....

CLAP! CLAP! CLAP! CLAP! CLAP! CLAP! CLAP! CLAP! CLAP! CLAP! CLAP! CLAP! CLAP! CLAP! CLAP!

MILLAR/HINDS

YES, DICK, AND THE OFFERS FROM THE ICE SHOWS REFLECT THAT...

US CAN FIN USSR UK E GER JAP ITALY

FANTASY ON ICE $1.1 MILLION | ICE PARADE $0.9 MILLION | FROZEN FOLLIES $0.75 MILLION

SINCE THE SUMMER GAMES ARE PROBABLY DOWN THE TUBE, THE STARS OF THE WINTER GAMES CAN NAME THEIR OWN PRICE FOR ENDORSEMENT CONTRACTS.

MOOSE NOSE BEER

IT'S THE MEGAHYPE AGENCY. THEY'RE BIDDING UP THE PRICES.

MILLAR/HINDS

IT'S RIDICULOUS. I READ THAT EVEN A BRONZE IN THE LUGE IS GOING FOR A MILLION-TWO...

MOOSE NOSE BEER

AR-NEE, AR-NEE, AR-NEE

ARNIE, BETTER PUT ON YOUR MEDALS AGAIN. IT'S ANOTHER MOB OF PEOPLE CALLING FOR YOU.

MILLAR HINDS

FUNNY. THEY'RE ALL WAVING BUNDLES OF PAPER...

ENDORSEMENT CONTRACTS.

OKAY, SOMEBODY AT THE PRESS CONFERENCE IS CERTAIN TO ASK ARNIE ABOUT MAKING MONEY OFF HIS SIX GOLD MEDALS.

SO ARNIE ANSWERS: 'GOSH, I DON'T KNOW ANYTHING ABOUT THAT STUFF, I JUST WANT TO BE A FOREST RANGER.'

I LIKE IT. IT'S CUTE. NOT EVEN AN 8-YEAR-OLD IS GONNA BELIEVE IT, BUT IT'S CUTE...

OKAY, ARNIE, WHAT IF AT YOUR PRESS CONFERENCE SOMEONE ASKS: 'WHAT KEPT YOU GOING TOWARD WINNING THAT SIXTH GOLD MEDAL?'

KNOWING THAT THE DIFFERENCE BETWEEN FIVE AND SIX GOLD MEDALS WAS WORTH A COOL MILLION IN MY BASIC AGENCY CONTRACT.

GOOD, ARNIE. GOOD. DIRECT ANSWERS ARE THE BEST KIND.

NOW, LET'S WORK AT MAKING THEM DIRECT IN A SLIGHT-LY DIFFERENT WAY.

YEP, WE SIGNED HIM. THE OLYMPIC SIX-MEDAL WINNER. WE'RE OPEN FOR BUSINESS.

HE'S A NICE KID. OPEN. NAIVE. WE'RE GONNA KEEP THAT IMAGE BY HAVING HIM ENDORSE ONLY PRODUCTS HE REALLY **BELIEVES** IN...

...SURE, HE BELIEVES IN THAT...

...GOLLY, THAT TOO...

...I CAN'T BE**LIEVE** THESE CO**IN**CIDENCES!

HERE'S SOMETHING NEW IN THE TINY-TYPE SCOREBOARD COLUMN...

SALE
FIREARM WAREHOUSE

FIRE SALE

Scoreboard
Boxing casualties........232
bouts........................96
KOs
permanent injuries.......17

Ice Hockey

NHL

LOOK, ANOTHER FIGHTER HAS BEEN PERMANENTLY DISABLED.

STATE BOXING COMM...

I MEAN, DON'T WE HAVE A PROBLEM?

OH, NOT REALLY.

STATE BOXING COMMISSION

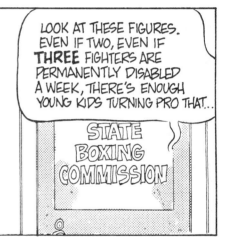

LOOK AT THESE FIGURES. EVEN IF TWO, EVEN IF **THREE** FIGHTERS ARE PERMANENTLY DISABLED A WEEK, THERE'S ENOUGH YOUNG KIDS TURNING PRO THAT...

STATE BOXING COMMISSION

...AND I KNOW WHAT YOU BLEEDING HEARTS ARE GONNA SAY: BAN BOXING.

SPORTS Section

BOXING TRAGEDY

LOOK, LIFE MAKES NO GUARANTEES. YOU COULD GET KILLED CROSSING THE STREET...

COLD DRINK

...ESPECIALLY IF WHILE YOU WERE CROSSING THE STREET SOMEONE WERE HITTING YOU ON THE HEAD AS HARD AS HE COULD.

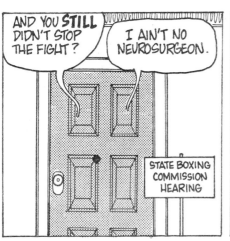

BONG!

RRRROUND SEVEN!

...WHAT'S THE POINT? THIS GUY'S TOO GOOD FOR ME...

I **COULD** FIGHT SEVEN MORE ROUNDS...GIVE THE FANS WHAT THEY PAID FOR...

ON THE OTHER HAND, I COULD BE BACK IN THE HOTEL IN TIME FOR JOHNNY CARSON...

...THE IRONY OF ALL THIS IS THAT WHILE I'M GETTING MY BRAINS BEATEN OUT...

...MY $8 MILLION PURSE FOR THE FIGHT IS ALREADY DEPOSITED IN MY BANK...

BONG!

RRROUND EIGHT!

I GOT THE COMMERCIAL CONTRACTS...I GOT MY $8 MILLION GUARANTEE ALREADY DEPOSITED IN MY BANK...

I GOT EVERYTHING I NEED.

WHAP!

--EXCEPT A PLAUSIBLE REASON TO QUIT BEFORE THIS GUY KILLS ME

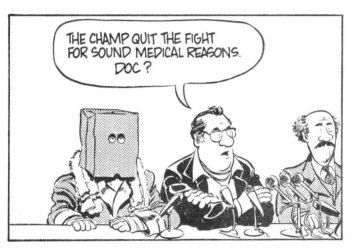

...WILL HE SKIP HIS LAST YEAR OF COLLEGE TO SIGN A $2 MILLION PRO BASKETBALL CONTRACT?

...JUST HOW DOES MELVIN QUALIFY AS A 'HARDSHIP CASE'?

WHY, THE POOR KID WANTS $2 MILLION, AND HE DOESN'T HAVE IT.

GEE, I SHOULD HAVE REALIZED.

DON'TCHA HAVE ANY FEELINGS?

...JUST HOW DOES MELVIN QUALIFY AS AN NBA 'HARDSHIP CASE' WHEN HIS FATHER EARNS $100,000 A YEAR?

NATIONAL BASKETBALL ASSOCIATION

Legal Department

TANK, THE STUFFERS' FRANCHISE IS IN TROUBLE. THEY CAN'T WAIT UNTIL MELVIN GRADUATES FROM COLLEGE FOR A BIG GATE ATTRACTION.

SO THEN IT WASN'T MELVIN WHO WAS DECLARED THE HARDSHIP CASE.

RULES ARE MADE TO BE INTERPRETED, TANK.

OKAY, MELVIN. WE'LL PAY YOU $2 MILLION, AND THAT'S OUR FINAL OFFER.

NBA STUFFERS

General Manager

UH, BERNIE, MELVIN WAS NEVER REALLY ACADEMICALLY STRONG IN MATH. YOU HAVE TO BARGAIN WITH HIM IN TERMS HE CAN RELATE TO.

OKAY, MELVIN, WE'LL PAY YOU THE EQUIVALENT OF 287 BUICK ELECTRAS, AND THAT'S OUR—

325, MINIMUM.

MILLAR/HINDS

WHAT IS IT THE COLLEGE PAYS THE SCHOLARSHIP JOCKS' 'ACADEMIC COUNSELOR' TO DO?

MILLAR/HINDS

DEPARTMENT OF INTERCOLLEGIATE ATHLETICS

ACADEMIC COUNSELOR

WILLIE, I'VE GOT YOUR PROFESSOR TO COMPROMISE. IF YOU'LL JUST SHOW UP IN CLASS -- JUST SHOW **UP**, THAT'S ALL -- AT LEAST ONCE A MONTH...

OH.

DEPARTMENT INTERCOLLEGIATE ATHLETICS

ACADEMIC COUNSELOR

YOUR JOB IS TO KEEP MY ATHLETES SCHOLASTICALLY ELIGIBLE. WHY IS MY STAR CENTER ABOUT TO FLUNK OUT?

COACH, HE'S JUST NOT ABLE TO KEEP UP WITH THE OTHER STUDENTS.

ACADEMIC COUNSELOR

ISN'T HE TAKING PHYS-ED CLASSES?

YES, BUT—

MILLAR/HINDS

HE CAN'T PASS 'THEORY AND PRACTICE OF COUNTING TO 100 BY TWOS'?

HE'S DOING ALL RIGHT IN LECTURE, BUT THE LAB WORK IS KILLING HIM.

MULVANEY, YOU'RE LATE FOR AFTERNOON PRACTICE AND YOU MISSED MORNING PRACTICE YESTERDAY! WHERE WERE YOU?

COACH, I UH—

TELL THE TRUTH.

I SNEAKED OFF AND WENT TO CLASS.

MILLAR/HINDS

MULVANEY, LET ME TRY TO EXPLAIN AGAIN THE THEORY BEHIND FALSIFIED TRANSCRIPTS...

THEY'RE VOTING IN THERE TO SEE IF THEY PUT THE COACH ON SUSPENSION.

THE ONE WHO THREW THE FOLDING CHAIR AT THE REFEREE?

THE RESULT SEEMS TO BE IN.

THE LEAGUE JUST PUT THE STUFFERS' COACH ON SUSPENSION.

THE ONE WHO THREW THE 24-SECOND CLOCK AT THE REFEREES?

REFEREE'S SSING ROOM

NO ADMITTANCE

HEY, I GUESS WE WON'T NEED THESE TONIGHT.

NO, IT IS **NOT** AN ALL-WHITE SCHOOL.

BROTHER CHARISMA UNIVERSITY

I HAPPEN TO KNOW THAT WE HAVE FIVE BLACK STUDENTS ON CAMPUS.

THE STARTING BASKETBALL TEAM?

ACTUALLY, ONE IS A RESERVE.

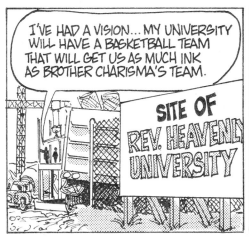

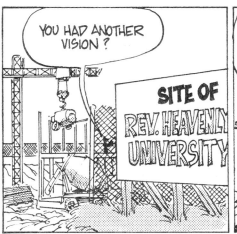

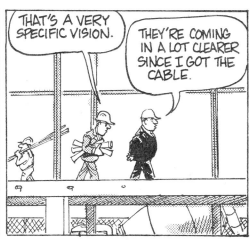

THE FEDERAL TRADE COMMISSION CONTINUES TO CHECK TO SEE IF ATHLETES REALLY USE PRODUCTS THEY ENDORSE...

ON THE SPOT NEWS

IN A HIGH-SPEED CHASE TODAY, THE FTC SWAT TEAM CAUGHT UP WITH A WELL-KNOWN QUARTERBACK...

...BEFORE HE WAS ABLE TO GET TO A DISCOUNT STORE TO PURCHASE THE KIND OF POPCORN POPPER FOR WHICH...

...AND YOU STILL CLAIM THAT YOU ATE FLAKEIES © EVERY DAY DURING YOUR TRAINING?

ABSOLUTELY.

FEDERAL TRADE COMMISSION

Athletic Endorsement Compliance Field Officer

OF THESE THREE DRY CEREALS, PLEASE BE SO KIND AS TO POINT TO THE BOWL OF FLAKEIES ©...

HEL-LO LEAVENWORTH...

WE CONFIRMED THAT IT WAS O.J. SIMPSON'S RESIDENCE...

FEDERAL TRADE COMMISSION
Athletic Endorsement Compliance Squad
FTC

...PROCEEDED DIRECTLY TO THE KITCHEN AND OPENED THE FREEZER COMPARTMENT.

AND?

--AND THE BIGGEST CAN OF TREE-SWEET YOU EVER SAW ROLLED OUT AND HIT ME ON THE TOE.

RATS.

WE'RE GOING AFTER A DIFFERENT KIND OF BEER DRINKER FROM THE GUYS WHO BUY 'LIGHTS.'

WELL, OUR NFL BROADCASTS ARE THE PERFECT PLACE TO INTRODUCE IT. WHAT'S IT CALLED?

'HEAVY.' BY THE WAY, ALL THE COMMERCIALS HAVE TO RUN BY THE END OF THE FIRST HALF.

MARKET RESEARCH TELLS US THAT AFTER THEN, THEY EXPECT THE AVERAGE 'HEAVY' DRINKER WILL BE UNCONSCIOUS.

WE'LL INTRODUCE YOUR NEW BEER ON TV SPORTS BROADCASTS.

HARD-CORE SPORTS: PRO FOOTBALL, NOT COLLEGE.

WE'RE REACHING THE TWO-FISTED BLUE-COLLAR BEER DRINKER WHO THINKS 'LIGHT' BEERS ARE SISSY, BUT WHO'S STILL WORRIED ABOUT HIS WEIGHT.

HOW'S THIS?

"NEW 'HEAVY': IT KNOCKS YOU OUT BEFORE IT FILLS YOU UP."

HOW ARE WE GOING TO SELL NEW 'HEAVY' BEER?

WELL, THERE'S THE COMEDY COMMERCIALS WITH THE WASHED-UP JOCKS...

THAT'S THE BIGGEST CLICHE IN ADVERTISING.

TIRED, TIRED, TIRED.

DONE TO DEATH.

EVERY AD AGENCY IN THE COUNTRY IS ON THAT BANDWAGON.

SO. WASHED-UP JOCKS IT IS...

WE CAN'T FIND **ANYBODY** TO DO THE COMMERCIALS?

THERE'S A CRITICAL SHORTAGE OF WASHED-UP JOCKS!

HEAVY BEER

THEY'RE SIGNED FOR BEER COMMERCIALS FASTER THAN THEY CAN BE WASHED UP!

WE NEED SOME WASHED-UP JOCKS FOR OUR NEW 'HEAVY' BEER COMMERCIALS, BUT THEY'RE ALL COMMITTED TO OTHER BEERS.

WE'RE HOPING THAT YOU COULD...AH, PERSUADE SOME TO AH...UMM...

IS THERE SOME EUPHEMISM I SHOULD USE, OR DO THEY SAY 'DEFECT' IN THE CIA TOO?

IT'LL BE $5,000 A HEAD. AND I KEEP TELLING YOU, I WAS AN AGRICULTURAL ATTACHE.

YOU HIRED A HEADHUNTER TO GET JOCKS TO DEFECT FROM 'LITE' BEER TO OUR COMMERCIALS?

HE OUGHT TO KNOW WHAT HE'S DOING. HE WAS IN THE CIA FOR 20 YEARS...

WILLIE, YOU'RE IN OUT OF THE COLD AT LAST.

HOW WOULD YOU LIKE TO BE PAID? KRUGERRANDS? DIAMONDS?

A CHECK TO MY AGENT IS COOL, MAN.

MILLAR/HINDS

IT'S OUR HEADHUNTER, CALLING FROM LA! HE GOT WILLIE WASHINGTON! THE FIRST DEFECTION FROM 'LITE'!

HE'LL BE IN MIAMI TOMORROW TO DO HIS FIRST 'HEAVY' BEER COMMERCIAL!

YOUR NAME IS GRUBER. YOU'RE A SALESMAN OF HEAVY INDUSTRIAL EQUIPMENT. THIS IS A PANAMANIAN PASSPORT AND $1,000 IN NEW JERSEY MONEY...

WILLIE WASHINGTON HAS DEFECTED! HE SHOOTS OUR FIRST 'HEAVY' BEER COMMERCIAL TODAY...

...RIGHT AFTER HE'S DEBRIEFED...

...WHERE WAS THE 'LITE' BEER ALUMNI COMMERCIAL SHOT..?

...WAS IT REALLY ALL YOU WANTED IN A BEER..?

...WHAT WOULD YOU ESTIMATE ARE LITE'S STRATEGIC RESERVES OF COMMERCIAL-READY WASHED-UP JOCKS..?

SURE, I USED TO DRINK ONE OF THOSE SISSY 'LIGHT' BEERS.

BUT THEN I REALIZED I OUGHTA BE DRINKIN' THAT STUFF WITH A STRAW.

THAT'S WHY I'VE SWITCHED TO 'HEAVY.' BECAUSE WILLIE WASHINGTON WANTS A BEER THAT PUTS UP A FIGHT.

...AND THIS TIME, WILLIE, COULD YOU SNARL A LITTLE?

HEAVY BEER AD
TAKE 5

...HIS COCAINE HABIT FINALLY RESULTED IN THE TRAGEDY IN THE STUFFERS' DRESSING ROOM...

...AND I WAS SO LOADED, MAN, I HAD FORGOTTEN THAT I KEPT THE **COKE** IN THE **FOOT**-POWDER CAN...

...ALL THREE KINDS OF ATHLETE'S FOOT FUNGUS MUST HAVE DIED **VERY** MELLOW...

...AND WAS YOUR USE OF COCAINE JUST AS HEAVY THROUGH YOUR TEAM'S CHAMPIONSHIP SEASON..?

HUH? CHAMPIONSHIP? DID YOU SAY **CHAMPIONSHIP**? I REMEMBER **SOME** KIND OF GAMES AFTER THE SEMIS, BUT... WOW, MAN, WE WON THE **CHAMPIONSHIP**?!?!

...APPARENTLY, EVEN HEAVIER.

HEY, WHERE'S THE CHAM**PAGNE**..?

...WHO WAS ARRESTED IN POSSESSION OF MORE THAN 12 POUNDS OF COCAINE...

ON THE SPOT NEWS

THE NFL LEAGUE OFFICE TOOK NO ACTION, SAYING THAT THE INCIDENT 'HAD NO BEARING ON HIS ACTIVITIES AS A PLAYER.'

ON THE SPOT NEWS

THE LEAGUE OFFICE ALSO ANNOUNCED A 'GET TOUGH' CAMPAIGN, INVOLVING HEAVY FINES, AGAINST PLAYERS WHO LET THEIR SHIRTTAILS HANG OUT....

...AND NOW, TANK, AFTER YOU WAKE UP...

...YOU WILL BE ABLE TO READ YOUR SPORTSCAST PERFECTLY...

MILLAR/HINDS

PITTSBURGH PIRATES PICKED A PECK OF PICKLED PEPPERS.

OH THANK YOU, **THANK** YOU!

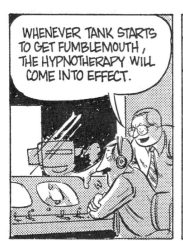

WHENEVER TANK STARTS TO GET FUMBLEMOUTH, THE HYPNOTHERAPY WILL COME INTO EFFECT.

AND HERE'S TANK McNAMARA WITH THE SPORTS NEWS...

THE...

MILLAR/HINDS

...AND WHEN YOU SEE THE LITTLE RED LIGHT ON TOP OF THE TV CAMERA, YOU WILL NOT BE A FUMBLEMOUTH...

MILLAR/HINDS

HEY, TANK, YOU DIDN'T FUMBLEMOUTH AT ALL!

MANKS TERRY VUTCH.

YANKS MERRY TOUCH!

PANKS PRERRY PUTCH!

GALX... SKLURX...

.....OKAY, DOC, BUT WHAT DO WE DO WHEN THE LITTLE RED LIGHT GOES **OFF**?!?

TICKETS

TENNIS
TOURNAMENT
QUARTERFINALS
John McEnroe
vs.
Ilie Nastase

THIS TENNIS
MATCH HAS BEEN
RATED [R]
No one under 17
admitted without
parent or guardian

TICKETS

TENNIS
TOURNAMENT
QUARTERFINALS
John McEnroe
vs.
Ilie Nastase

TANK, McENROE FOUGHT BACK WITH A VERY EFFECTIVE SNARL AT THE UMPIRE...

BUT THEN HE COULDN'T HANDLE NASTASE'S VICIOUS FOREHAND ABUSE OF THE LINE JUDGE...

MILLAR/HINDS

IN RESPONSE TO THE PLAYERS' COMBINED DEMANDS, IT WAS AGREED...

MILLAR/HINDS

THAT THE SEMIFINAL MATCH BETWEEN JOHN McENROE AND JIMMY CONNORS WOULD BE PLAYED BEFORE NO SPECTATORS, NO MEDIA, NO LINE JUDGES AND NO UMPIRE.

WHEN ASKED WHEN THE TOURNAMENT OFFICIALS WOULD KNOW WHO WON, THE PLAYERS SAID...

QUOTE, WHEN ONE OF US SHOWS UP FOR THE FINALS, DUMMY, UNQUOTE.

MR. BORG DEFEATS MR. CONNORS, 6-LOVE, 6-LOVE, 6-LOVE.

JIMMY HATES TO HANG AROUND AFTER HE LOSES...

...NOW DOWN TO BUD COLLINS WHO HAS AN INTERVIEW WITH JIMMY CONNORS...

NOPE. BACK TO YOU, TANK.

...AND WHO'S YOUR FAVORITE PLAYER?

MARTINA!

MINE'S BJORN BORG.

TIMMY AND RALPHIE LOOK UP TO JIMMY CONNORS AND JOHN McENROE...

AND NOW YOUR SON, AS PROMISED, WILL RECEIVE INSTRUCTION FROM INTERNATIONAL SUPERSTAR ZXWVITSZI PSEUDOZWCITZWIKI.

WOOTI VLAGIC GIBBERDOOSKI VICH GLBDNRBIIK.EU VSUENN KVETCH DOBBERNICH...EK DOBBERNICH VON DEEBLHAU FRON BETL KOBBERINK. FROGHN? EK FROGHN?..

I'M PAYING 800 BUCKS FOR A WEEK OF **THAT**?

HEH HEH, ACTUALLY, MR. PSEUDOZWCITZWIKI TEACHES, AH, MORE BY **EXAMPLE**...

MY SON AND THE OTHER KIDS RECEIVED 'PERSONAL INSTRUCTION' FROM YOUR PRO FOOTBALL SUPERSTAR FOR EXACTLY THREE AND A HALF MINUTES!

BUT SHARING THREE AND A HALF MINUTES OF THE FOOTBALL GENIUS OF BUCK BAKER IS LIKE WEEKS WITH A LESSER LIGHT!

BOBBY, JUST THINK HOW VALUABLE WHAT BUCK BAKER PASSED ON TO YOU WILL BE ALL THROUGH YOUR LIFE IN SPORTS.

Top Pro Total Sports SUMMER CAMP

HOW TO GET A STEWARDESS' PHONE NUMBER BY CALLING THE AIRLINES AND PRETENDING IT'S AN EMERGENCY?

...MAYBE NOT OF IMMEDIATE VALUE, GRANTED...

IF IT'S A LONG STRIKE, IT COULD TURN VIOLENT...

Bashers PROFESSIONAL BASEBALL

HOW DO YOU KNOW THAT WHOEVER THREW IT WAS A STRIKER?

BECAUSE IT WAS A SLIDER, WITH GOOD VELOCITY, THAT MOVED DOWN AND IN.

MILLAR/HINDS

TANK, I VOTED FOR THE STRIKE, AND IF IT HAPPENS, I'M 100 PER CENT FOR IT. IT'S FOR THE FUTURE OF THE YOUNG PLAYERS.

DOESN'T YOUR CONTRACT STIPULATE THAT YOU'LL BE PAID WHETHER THERE'S A STRIKE OR NOT?

THAT DOESN'T AFFECT MY PRINCIPLES ONE BIT, TANK. I'LL BE WILLING TO SIT IT OUT UNTIL DOOMSDAY IF THAT'S WHAT IT TAKES TO GET A CONTRACT WE CAN LIVE WITH.

AND IF WE DO STRIKE, WE GO STANDING TOGETHER IN SOLIDARITY AND BROTHERHOOD!

MILLAR/HINDS

...THE CUBS AND THE DODGERS HAVE NOW LINKED ARMS AND ARE MARCHING OFF THE FIELD, SINGING 'THE INTERNATIONALE'...

IF THERE IS A STRIKE, WILL YOU BE ON THE STREET, CARRYING A SIGN?

IN THAT HOT SUN?

THE PLAYERS' ASSOCIATION HAS A SENIORITY SYSTEM. VETERANS WITH FIVE YEARS MAJOR LEAGUE SERVICE AND WITH SALARIES ABOVE $1 MILLION...

...CAN USE DESIGNATED PICKETS.

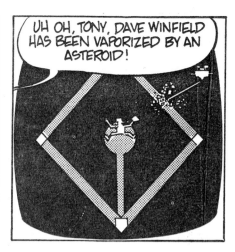

ON-THE-SPOT NEWS HAS LEARNED THAT BASEBALL OWNERS ARE SECRETLY TRAINING JAPANESE IMPOSTERS IN CASE THE PLAYERS STRIKE...

ON THE SPOT SPORTS

AMAZING! THAT'S **EXACTLY** REGGIE JACKSON'S HOME-RUN TROT...

...THAT IS NOT, HOWEVER, REGGIE JACKSON'S 'HIGH FIVE...'

THAT'S A JAPANESE BALLPLAYER MADE UP TO LOOK LIKE MIKE SCHMIDT?

THEY'RE TRAINING HIM TO DO POST-GAME INTERVIEWS IN CASE OF A BASEBALL STRIKE.

...AH YUST TLYING TO MEET BRALL, BUT I ROOK UP LOUNDING FRUST AND SEE UMPAH DOING RISS...

...SO THEN THE PLAYERS AREN'T WORRIED THE OWNERS MIGHT TRY JAPANESE IMPOSTERS IF YOU STRIKE?

TANK, BASEBALL IS AN AMERICAN INVENTION. AN AMERICAN INSTITUTION. AMERICAN BASEBALL FANS DEMAND THE AMERICAN PRODUCT.

NICE-LOOKING KWASIMOTO Z-34 YOU HAVE THERE.

...THEY'RE ALL I DRIVE. GOT ONE FOR THE WIFE, TOO...

SOME STRIKING BASEBALL PLAYERS ARE LOOKING FOR OTHER SOURCES OF INCOME

ON THE SPOT SPORTS

FOOD STAMP APPLICATIONS

YES, UNFORTUNATELY, THE INCOME FROM THE STOCK PORTFOLIO AND THE ARIZONA CONDOS DO FIGURE INTO YOUR BASE INCOME...

MILLAR/HINDS

FIRST THING IS TO ACQUAINT YOU WITH WHAT PEOPLE IN THE 'REAL WORLD' MAKE...

TURQUOISE ROOM

MAJOR LEAGUE PLAYERS' ASSN. STRIKE SERVICE

Temporary Job Services

MILLAR/HINDS

I'M PASSING OUT A LIST OF THE AVERAGE MONTHLY SALARIES OF PIPEFITTERS, TEACHERS, FIREFIGHTERS...

TURQUOISE ROOM

MAJOR LEAGUE PLAYERS' ASSN. STRIKE SERVICE

Temporary Job Services

...HEY, WRONG LIST...

GOTTA BE THEIR PER DIEMS...

...AREN'T THERE A BUNCH OF ZEROS MISSING?

MAJOR LEAGUE PLAYERS' ASSN. STRIKE SERVICE

Temporary Job Services

STRIKING BALLPLAYERS, GETTING INTO THE SPIRIT OF LABOR UNREST, OVERTURNED A CAR.

ON THE SPOT SPORTS

THAT'S WHAT STRIKERS ARE ALWAYS DOING ON TV, AND IT LOOKED LIKE FUN.

MILLAR/HINDS

YOU DONATED THE CAR DIDN'T YOU?

YEAH, IT WAS JUST THE '72 MERCEDES AND THE CLUTCH WAS SHOT ANYWAY...

THE BASEBALL STRIKE FIGURES TO HURT MORE THAN JUST THE BASEBALL PLAYERS AND THE OWNERS...

ON THE SPOT SPORTS

SHANGHAI TEMPORARY LABOR

HE BET ON A MAJOR LEAGUE BASEBALL GAME? BUT ISN'T THERE A STRIKE?

HE BET ON A REBROADCAST OF THE FIFTH GAME OF THE 1975 WORLD SERIES.

I HAD FORGOTTEN HOW IT CAME OUT, SO THAT MEANT THERE WAS A REASONABLE CHANCE MY BOOKIE HAD TOO...

AS THE BASEBALL STRIKE ENTERS ITS SECOND WEEK...

...OFFICIALS IN TOWNS WITH MINOR LEAGUE TEAMS ARE BRACING FOR HORDES OF REFUGEE FANS FROM METROPOLITAN AREAS...

WE'RE DOING WHAT WE CAN FOR REFUGEE BASEBALL FANS...

...BUT OUR MINOR LEAGUE PARK ONLY HOLDS 4,000...

BREAKS YOUR HEART. SOME OF THESE PEOPLE HAVE GONE 13, 14 DAYS WITHOUT A POPUP...

...EMERGENCY SHIPMENTS OF CHEAP PLASTIC BATTING HELMETS HAVE BEEN SENT TO THE BASEBALL FAN REFUGEE CAMPS NEAR ROCHESTER...

10,000 UNITS ISN'T ENOUGH, GOVERNOR! UNLESS THIS WEATHER BREAKS AND THEY CAN AIRDROP THE WINDBREAKERS...

...IT'S GOING TO GET PRET-TY HAIRY...

THIS IS ONE OF THE CAMPS TEEMING WITH FANS FLEEING BIG CITIES IN SEARCH OF BASEBALL...

THIS MAN'S STORY IS TYPICALLY HEARTBREAKING.

YOU WERE SEPARATED FROM YOUR BROTHER, WEREN'T YOU?

YEAH. WHEN WE HEARD ON THE RADIO THAT I'D WON OUR BET ON WIMBLEDON, THE TURKEY DUCKED OUT THE BACK DOOR OF HOJO'S...

CATCH IT!

HOW ABOUT IT, GUYS? COMPENSATION?

NOPE.

WE'VE AGREED NOT TO UPSET THE DELICACY OF THE NEGOTIATIONS BY DISCUSSING THEM AT THIS STAGE...

REMEMBER WHEN YOU COULD OWN A PLAYER BODY AND SOUL?

PLAYER-OWNER NEGOTIATION

YEAH. IF HE GAVE YOU ANY TROUBLE, YOU COULD CRUSH HIS SPIRIT LIKE A PAPER CUP AND DRIVE HIM OUT OF THE GAME.

(SIGH) BASEBALL WAS FUN THEN...

...ATTENDANCE IS UP, TELEVISION CONTRACTS ARE FATTER.

RAY GREBEY
BASEBALL OWNERS REP.

HOW CAN BASEBALL OWNERS CLAIM FINANCIAL HARDSHIP? WHENEVER A TEAM'S UP FOR SALE, THERE ARE LINES OF POTENTIAL BUYERS.

BUT HOW MUCH LONGER, TANK? LIKE OIL, THERE'S A FINITE SUPPLY OF SUCKERS.

BASEBALL TEAMS HAVE HISTORICALLY BEEN PLAYTHINGS OF THE RICH...

RAY GREBEY
BASEBALL OWNERS REP.

...AND YOU'RE SIMPLY TRYING TO KEEP THE PLAYERS FROM BECOMING RICHER THAN THE OWNERS?

TANK, FANS CHERISH THE GREAT TRADITIONS MORE IN BASEBALL THAN ANY OTHER PRO SPORT...

IF WE LOSE THIS BATTLE, IT'S JUST A SMALL STEP TO ALUMINUM BATS...

THERE'S A LOYAL BASEBALL FAN. STRIKE OR NO STRIKE, EVERY DAY HE LOOKS AT THE STANDINGS...

NOW WAIT A MINUTE...

...THE SMASHERS HAVE MOVED FROM FIFTH TO THIRD.

ALTHOUGH HIS OFFICE IS INVESTIGATING ALLEGATIONS THAT DURING THE STRIKE THE SMASHERS SNEAKED FROM FIFTH TO THIRD PLACE IN THE STANDINGS...

...INSIDERS BELIEVE THE BASEBALL COMMISSIONER WILL DUCK A CONFRONTATION WITH THE SMASHERS.

MR. COMMISSIONER, HERE IS AN ENLARGEMENT FROM THE WASHINGTON STAR SPORTS SECTION OF JUNE 8, 1981. COMPARE THIS WITH--

C'MON, SON, THESE ARE SERIOUS ALLEGATIONS. I WANT FACTS, NOT HEARSAY...

HAVE THE SMASHERS BEEN CAUGHT RED-HANDED SNEAKING UP TWO PLACES IN THE NATIONAL LEAGUE STANDINGS DURING THE BASEBALL STRIKE? AND WILL THE COMMISSIONER CONFRONT THE TEAM'S POWERFUL OWNER...?

ON THE SPOT SPORTS

MR. COMMISSIONER, GRANTED THAT THE OWNERS PAY YOUR SALARY, AND GRANTED THAT WE DON'T WANT TO BE HASTY...

OFFICE OF THE COMMISSIONER

OKAY, OKAY. WE DID IT...

OFFICE OF THE COMMISSIONER

...THE SMASHERS CONFESS. WE TRIED TO SNEAK FROM FIFTH PLACE TO THIRD PLACE IN THE STANDINGS DURING THE STRIKE.

HOW ON EARTH DID YOU THINK YOU COULD GET AWAY WITH SOMETHING LIKE THAT IN FRONT OF MILLIONS OF PEOPLE?

WE GOT THE IDEA FROM THE GUY WHO FINISHED FIRST AT THIS YEAR'S INDY 500...

THE PUBLIC THINKS OF US AS MONEY-GRUBBING JOCKS WHO'RE HOLDING THE NATIONAL PASTTIME HOSTAGE.

PROPERTY OF THE PLAYERS UNION

FACE IT, GUYS. THE STRIKE REALLY HURT OUR IMAGE.

PROPERTY OF THE PLAYERS UNION

MILLAR/HINDS

PROPERTY OF THE PLAYERS UNION

WELL, IT LOOKS LIKE SOMEBODY HAD BETTER GO VISIT ANOTHER CHILDREN'S WARD.

I'LL ALERT THE MEDIA.

PROPERTY OF THE PLAYERS UNION

YOU GENTLEMEN MUST BE THE PLAYERS FROM THE SMASHERS, COME TO VISIT THE CHILDREN.

CHILDREN'S WARD

...THE BASEBALL STRIKE'S GIVEN US A PUBLIC IMAGE AS MONEY-GRUBBING JOCKS, BUT...

UH, MA'AM, YOU HAVEN'T SEEN A BUNCH OF CAMERAMEN FROM THE LOCAL TV STATIONS, HAVE YOU?

MILLAR/HINDS

RELAX, THEY PHONED AND SAID THEY'D BE LATE. WOULD YOU GENTLEMEN CARE TO WAIT IN THE PARENTS' LOUNGE...?

HAROLD, A FAMOUS PERSON IS HERE VISITING THE KIDS IN THE WARD, AND HE WANTS TO MEET **YOU**.

OF ALL THE FAMOUS PEOPLE IN THE WORLD, HAROLD, WHO WOULD YOU LIKE TO SEE THE MOST?

CARL SAGAN? GEE, IS CARL **SAGAN** HERE!??

STOP THE TAPE.

MILLAR/HINDS

I DIDN'T MEAN TO HURT HIS FEELINGS, BUT I DON'T KNOW THAT MUCH ABOUT BASEBALL...

THAT KID MUST NOT BE AN AMERICAN...

AREN'T THERE ANY KIDS WHO'RE, LIKE, IN A BODY CAST...?

SEE? SEE? THAT'S THE KIND OF GUYS PRO ATHLETES ARE.

THEY'VE BEEN ON STRIKE, WITHOUT PAY...

...AND THEY STILL HAVE TIME TO VISIT SICK KIDS IN THE HOSPITAL.

MOTHER TERESA, MOVE OVER.

BASEBALL'S IMAGE IS TARNISHED ENOUGH. WHEN WE ANNOUNCE THE BASEBALL STRIKE IS OVER...

...LET'S SAY WHAT FINALLY GOT US TO AGREE WASN'T FINANCIAL ISSUES BUT A MUTUAL FEELING THAT AMERICANS DESERVED THEIR NATIONAL PASTIME BACK...

HONEST, GUYS, THEY'LL BUY IT. SURVEYS SHOW THAT AT LEAST 60 PER CENT OF AMERICANS BELIEVE IN THE EASTER BUNNY.

...YES, THE BASEBALL STRIKE'S OVER. BETTER ALERT THE POLICE.

PEOPLE ARE GOING TO POUR INTO THE STREETS IN THE BIGGEST EXPRESSION OF PUBLIC JOY SINCE V-E DAY.

UH, BOSS...

WE'RE IN SERIOUS TROUBLE.

PETE SIGNED TO PLAY IN THE BANANA LEAGUE.

DAY-O, DAY-O...

WHATAYA MEAN, THERE'S NO TELEPHONE? HOW DO I GET HOLD OF MY AGENT?

MOST GUYS PUT NOTES IN A BOTTLE.

I WANNA SEE THE MANAGER! WHEN I SIGNED, NOBODY TOLD ME THERE WERE 4,000-MILE ROAD TRIPS.

GOOD MORNING, MR. WASHINGTON, I AM 'PAPPY' SCHMIDT, THE MANAGER-OWNER, AND THIS IS HERR...ER, 'RED' BRATWURST, THE ZIRD BASE COACH...

HELLO, YOUALL.

...THE ARM, WATCH THE ARM...

YOU MISSED CURFEW, MR. WASHINGTON. THERE ARE ZEVERE...AH, SEVERE FINES FOR THAT.

THE BATTING CAGE.

HEHHEHHEHHEHHEH...

SO? A LITTLE EXTRA BATTING PRACTICE NEVER HURT ANYBODY.

HEHHEHHEHHEHHEH.

THE HALL-OF-FAMER SAID IN A PRESS RELEASE, QUOTE...

ON THE SPOT SPORTS

...BASEBALL'S BEEN VERY, VERY GOOD TO ME.

...BUT IT COULD BE BETTER, UNQUOTE.

...IT WAS STILL ANOTHER HONOR FOR THE HALL-OF-FAMER...

ON THE SPOT SPORTS

AT THE AWARDS BANQUET, IN A DEPARTURE FROM THE USUAL CLICHED, SELF-EFFACING ACCEPTANCE SPEECH, THE FORMER SLUGGING CHAMP SAID:

ABOUT ALL I CAN SAY IS, IT'S ABOUT TIME.

...THE HALL-OF-FAMER SLUGGING CHAMP FEELS THAT HIS CONTRIBUTION AS A PLAYER HAS NOT BEEN ADEQUATELY RECOGNIZED.

SPORTALK

LOOK, TANK, DON'T GET ME WRONG. I'M NOT SAYING THAT SISTER TERESA **DOESN'T** DESERVE IT...

SPORTALK

TANK, DID YOUR COLLEGE RETIRE YOUR NUMBER WHEN YOU GRADUATED?

UH...YES.

THEY SORT OF HAD TO. THEY COULDN'T GET ANYBODY ELSE TO WEAR IT.

HERE FROM THE SPEEDWAY IS A LIVE REPORT...

TANK, THOUSANDS OF STOCK CAR RACING FANS HERE WERE STUNNED TODAY...

...WHEN THE GOOD OL' BOY 500 WAS MARRED BY A LACK OF TRAGEDY...

YOUR COMPANY'S TRANSFERRED YOU INTO THE ARMPIT OF THE COUNTRY, FELLA...

IT'S EITHER TOO HOT, OR TOO COLD, AND THE NEAREST MOVIE THEATER IS 50 MILES AWAY....

HOWEVER, THERE IS A 24-HOUR ALL-SPORTS CHANNEL ON THE CABLE.

SOUNDS LIKE HEAVEN TO ME.

MILLAR/HINDS

.....COMING UP NEXT, AT 3 A.M.....

SPORTSNET
THE 24-HOUR
ALL-SPORTS
CABLE TV NETWORK
PRESENTS

....AUSTRALIAN RULES BASEBALL?

AFTER THE BATTER HITS THE BALL, HE RUNS TO THIRD INSTEAD OF FIRST.

JOCKS ENDORSING CANDIDATES IS A DYNAMITE IDEA....

...WE'RE INVENTORYING OUR CLIENTS TO FIND OUT WHO SUPPORTS WHO FOR PRESIDENT....

WELL, I ASKED BUCK IF HE WAS GOING TO VOTE FOR REAGAN OR CARTER.....

AND?

HE SAID: 'WHAT ARE THEY RUNNING FOR?'

PUT BUCK DOWN AS UNCOMMITTED.

THE SLUGGER, WHO'S HAD HIS SHARE OF RUN-INS WITH THE MEDIA, WANTS TO START HIS OWN NEWSPAPER COLUMN...

NOW YOU'RE SURE YOU CAN DO THIS...

NO SWEAT. I TOLD YOU, I TOOK TYPING IN THE EIGHTH GRADE...

MOST PLAYERS ACCEPT THE BETWEEN-INNINGS CLOWNING OF THE MASCOTS WITH A SENSE OF HUMOR...

ON THE SPOT NEWS

ON THE SPOT NEWS

...SOME DO NOT.

THE CHICKEN WAS DISCOVERED! I CAN BE DISCOVERED!

THOUSANDS OF PEOPLE ARE SAYING THAT ALL OVER THE COUNTRY! DON'T YOU REALIZE THE ODDS?

THERE'S A BROKEN HEART FOR EVERY STADIUM LIGHT IN YANKEE STADIUM!

I THINK THE SELF-APPOINTED MASCOTS SITUATION IS GETTING OUT OF HAND...

YEA TEAM

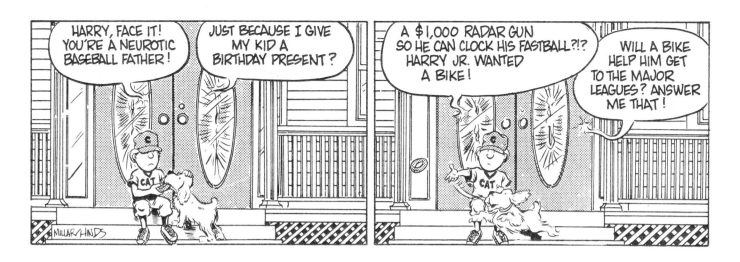

NOW A REPORT ON THE CLOSEST PENNANT RACE IN YEARS...

JIM, THE RAP IS THAT YOUR PLAYERS ARE CHOKING UNDER 'PENNANT PRESSURE.'

TANK, IT'S A CLOSE RACE, BUT THIS IS A VETERAN TEAM.

JUST TAKE A LOOK AROUND. DO YOU SEE ANYBODY ABOUT TO CHOKE?

PLEASE, PLEASE, DON'T MAKE ME PITCH TODAY!!

HOW DO THESE PROFESSIONALS HANDLE THE DREAD 'PENNANT PRESSURE'?

WELL, THIRD BASEMAN RED RIDGELY SLOWLY AND METHODICALLY BANGS HIS HEAD AGAINST THE SHOWER WALL...

THUMP THUMP THUMP

FOR CENTER FIELDER RAUL O'GONZALES, IT'S FUNNY HATS AND ANONYMOUS PHONE CALLS...

AND HERE'S THE LOCKER OF RESERVE CATCHER DANNY SCHWARTZ...

JIM, HOW DOES A MANAGER KEEP HIS TEAM FROM CRASHING UNDER THE DREAD 'PENNANT PRESSURE'?

TANK, IT'S A MATTER OF KNOWING HUMAN NATURE... KNOWING WHEN TO PRAISE, WHEN TO CRITICIZE... KEEPING THE GUYS LOOSE AND HAVING FUN...

AND MAKING SURE EVERYBODY KNOWS THAT IF THEY MESS UP, I'LL KILL THEM.

DO YOU TURKEYS HEAR THAT?!? I'VE GOT A .38, AND ANYBODY WHO CHOKES, WHO MISSES AN EASY GROUNDER, WHO...

ANITA, HERE'S WHAT I OWE FOR MY CHANCE IN THE WORLD SERIES POOL.

I COULD GET IN A LOT OF TROUBLE WHEN I WAS IN THE NFL, SO I STILL FEEL A LITTLE STRANGE, YOU KNOW, GAMBLING.

GOODNESS, TANK, 50 CENTS IN AN OFFICE WORLD SERIES POOL ISN'T REALLY--

FREEZE!

LEFKOWICZ, YOU CALLED THE VICE SQUAD BECAUSE YOU'VE DISCOVERED A WORLD **SERIES** POOL?

SORRY, FOLKS.

BUT LIEUTENANT, GAMBLING IS DESTROYING THE INTEGRITY OF SPORTS!

AN EAGER YOUNG COP BUSTED THE WORLD SERIES POOL?

YEAH. THE VICE SQUAD LIEUTENANT APOLOGIZED, BUT NOT BEFORE THE YOUNG COP HAD TANK SPREAD-EAGLED UP AGAINST THE WALL.

GEE, TANK, WE JUST WANT YOU TO KNOW THAT ALL OF US HERE CONSIDER THAT YOUR DEBT TO SOCIETY--

CUT. IT. OUT.

HERE, SCIENTISTS ARE TRYING TO FIND OUT...COULD THE WORLD SERIES BE PLAYED IN MONTREAL IN LATE OCTOBER...?

...WHERE DID IT GO...?

...I LOST IT IN A FLURRY...

YOU'RE STUDYING WALRUS MIGRATION..?

BEAT IT, I SAID.

KEEP OUT

IF THE WORLD SERIES WERE TO BE PLAYED IN MONTREAL IN LATE OCTOBER, I SEE TWO PUBLIC-RELATIONS APPROACHES TO THE PROBLEM...

THE FIRST IS TO GO AHEAD AND CONCEDE THAT MAYBE IT IS A LITTLE CHILLY.

...THE OTHER PUBLIC-RELATIONS APPROACH, WERE THE WORLD SERIES PLAYED IN MONTREAL, WOULD BE TO TRY PULLING A BOWIE KUHN.

YOU MEAN **PRETEND** THAT IT'S NOT COLD?

GOOD HEAVENS, MAN! IN REGULATION KANSAS CITY OR BALTIMORE UNIFORMS, IT WOULD BE TWO, THREE INNINGS AT MOST BEFORE UNCONSCIOUSNESS SETS IN!

SINCE BASEBALL IS A SUMMER GAME, THE COMMISSIONER WOULD INSIST ON WEARING SHIRTSLEEVES TO THE SERIES.

ICE LOCKER

ADMITTANCE ONLY TO AUTHORIZED PERSONNEL

CLEAR PETROLEUM JELLY, GENTLEMEN. ALL BUT INVISIBLE TO THE PRYING TELEVISION CAMERA, AND PROVEN BY GENERATIONS OF CHANNEL SWIMMERS...

THE COMMISSIONER WILL INSIST ON WEARING THIS TO THE WORLD SERIES, EVEN IF IT WERE PLAYED IN MONTREAL IN LATE OCTOBER. WE MUST PREPARE FOR THAT.

ELECTRIC UNDERWEAR!

...WE'D NEED TO RUN AT LEAST 40 AMPS THROUGH IT...

NIX, GENTLEMEN... THE MEDIA WILL GET SUSPICIOUS IF THE SNOW MELTS ON HIS SHOULDERS WHILE IT'S DRIFTING ON EVERYBODY ELSE'S...

THIS FILM SHOWS OUR SIMULATION OF GAME CONDITIONS WERE THE WORLD SERIES TO BE PLAYED IN MONTREAL...

DID THEY EVER FIND THAT POPUP?

THE RADIO BEEPER FAILED, MR. COMMISSIONER. MAYBE IN THE SPRING...

OH WELL, IT'S REALLY NO BIG DEAL. A FEW CHANGES IN THE GROUND RULES...

DO YOU REALLY THINK WOMEN SPORTSWRITERS WANT INTO THE LOCKER ROOMS JUST TO OGLE THE MEN?

HOME TEAM DRESSING ROOM NO ADMITTANCE

DRESSED, UNDRESSED. WE DON'T CARE. WE WANT QUOTES SO WE CAN MAKE OUR DEADLINES, JUST LIKE MALE REPORTERS.

DRESSING ROOM NO ADMITTANCE

AND IF STEVE GARVEY HAPPENS TO WANDER THROUGH IN A WET T-SHIRT...WELL, IT'S JUST A NICE BONUS...

MILLAR/HINDS

ESSING ROOM NO ADMITTAN

KID, IT'S BEEN A HARD FIGHT FOR WOMEN SPORTSWRITERS TO GET INTO THE MEN'S LOCKER ROOMS.

HOME TEAM DRESSING ROOM NO ADMITTAN

I'M A PROFESSIONAL, AND ALL I WANT TO DO IS MY JOB. I'VE BEEN LAUGHED AT, IGNORED, CONDESCENDED TO...

BUT HERE I AM. I'VE MADE IT.

HOME TEAM DRESSING

NOW IF I COULD JUST STOP FEELING LIKE I'M 12 YEARS OLD AND I'VE WALKED INTO THE WRONG RESTROOM...

MILLAR/HINDS

JANE, THIS IS A TERRIFIC POST-GAME INTERVIEW STORY.

SPORTS D

...ESPECIALLY TO HAVE BEEN WRITTEN UNDER THE PRESSURE OF THAT FIRST-TIME-FOR-WOMEN-IN-THE-DRESSING-ROOM SITUATION.

UH, BOSS. AM I THROUGH?

YEP.

IT IS OKAY FOR ME TO BE EMBARRASSED NOW?

FEEL FREE.

I COULD HAVE DIED!!

MILLAR/HINDS

HE SEEMS TO BE CRAZY ABOUT YOU.

BUT I WORK FOR A PAPER IN ANOTHER TOWN. HOW CAN WE HAVE A RELATIONSHIP? I'M ONLY HERE FOR FOUR GAMES A SEASON.

THERE'S ALWAYS THE PLAYOFFS.

ARE YOU KIDDING? WITH OUR BULLPEN AND NO CLUTCH HITTING?

THE GUY'S REALLY FALLEN FOR YOU, HUH?

I FEEL SO **GUILTY**. I COVERED TANK'S LAST GAME AS A PRO. HE LOOKED UP MY STORY IN HIS SCRAPBOOK.

THE RAMS GAINED 438 YARDS OVER TANK'S POSITION. I CALLED HIM 'THE HUMAN HIGHWAY STRIPE.' TANK SAID HE THOUGHT THAT WAS **CUTE**.

JANE, LOOK. FOR HIS SAKE, CALL IT OFF.

IT'S JUST A *LITTLE* LIE...

MY PAPER'S TAKING ME OFF BASEBALL TO COVER THE NEW— THE NEW—

...PRO LACROSSE TEAM.

BUT THERE'S NO TEAM HERE. WE'LL NEVER **SEE** EACH OTHER AGAIN!

A FRANCHISE IN THE NEW PRO LACROSSE LEAGUE ...VERY INTERESTING.

TANK, YOU **DO** UNDERSTAND THAT NORMALLY WE MAKE NEW CAR LOANS...

CREDIT UNION

...AND ANY LITTLE BOY, REGARDLESS OF RACE, CREED OR NATIONAL ORIGIN...

...HAS AN EQUAL CHANCE TO GROW UP TO BECOME THE NFL'S NUMBER-ONE DRAFT CHOICE.

LET'S SEE IF YOU CAN FIND **THAT** IN ANY COMMUNIST COUNTRY!!

RIGHT... YOU SAID IT ...I'LL DRINK TO THAT.

GET ME ON THE AIR!! THE NFL NUMBER-ONE DRAFT CHOICE HAS BEEN ANNOUNCED!!

CONTROL ROOM

BUT THE PRESIDENT IS DECLARING A STATE OF NATIONAL EMERG--

BREAK INTO IT!!

LEMME AT THOSE BUTTONS!!

...SPORTS IS BOB'S LIFE...

...NO, NO, NO!! THE RED CARPET ROLLS OUT, THE TRUMPETS SOUND, THE DOVES ARE RELEASED, **THEN** CUE THE MORMON TABERNACLE CHOIR...

GRAND BALLROOM

WHAT ARE THEY REHEARSING FOR IN THERE? THE ARRIVAL OF PRINCE CHARLES?

CLOSE. THE NFL'S NUMBER-ONE DRAFT CHOICE.

...WHITE! I WANT **WHITE** ROSE PETALS!

GRAND BALLROOM

THE TEAM OWNER SAYS HE CAN'T AFFORD TO PAY THE PLAYER'S PRICE. SAYS THE PLAYER'S AGENT....

ON THE SPOT SPORTS

MY CLIENT IS MORE THAN JUST A FOOTBALL PLAYER. HE'S A NATIONAL ASSET. THIS CITY SHOULD BE PROUD TO HAVE HIM.

ARE YOU SUGGESTING A BOND ELECTION TO PAY HIS SALARY?

IT SEEMS ENTIRELY APPROPRIATE. WE'RE TALKING THE NFL NUMBER-ONE DRAFT CHOICE, PEOPLE!

.....THE AGENT FOR THE NUMBER-ONE DRAFT PICK TODAY PROPOSED THAT THE CITY HOLD A BOND ELECTION TO PAY HIS $2-MILLION-A-YEAR SALARY DEMAND....

I KNOW THIS TOWN IS FOOTBALL-CRAZY. BUT THAT **HAS** TO BE A JOKE, RIGHT?

HONK! HONK! HONK! HONK! HONK!

WRONG.

HONK! HONK! HONK! HONK! HONK! HONK! HONK! HONK!

HONK IF WE PAY HIM

HIM

UH, BOSS, WE'VE TRADED AWAY MOST OF OUR EARLY CHOICES, REMEMBER?

NFL DRAFT TODAY
SPECTATOR'S AREA

WHAT ROUND IS OUR FIRST PICK?

THE, UH, 43RD....

THE SMASHERS HAVE TRADED AWAY ALL THEIR PICKS UNTIL THIS ROUND.

WE PICK AFTER GREEN BAY. BUT BY THIS TIME, THERE'S NOT GOING TO BE ANYBODY LEFT BUT OSCAR THE KICKING KANGAROO.

THE GREEN BAY PACKERS SELECT OSCAR THE KICKING KANGAROO.

BOSS, WE'VE GOT TO MAKE OUR DRAFT PICK.

THERE'S THIS TACKLE. SCOUTS SAY HE MIGHT BE A LITTLE HEAVY, THOUGH.

WHAT DOES HE CLOCK?

4.7 SECONDS

THAT'S PRETTY GOOD. FOR 40 YARDS?

NO, THAT'S HOW LONG IT TAKES A DEFENSIVE PLAYER TO RUN AROUND HIM. BOSS, IT'S THE 43RD ROUND....

WHAT HAVE YOU MISSED MOST SINCE RETIRING?

OH, I MISS THE CAMARADERIE...

...THE FEELING OF REBIRTH...

...THE CHALLENGE TO DO YOUR BEST...

...THE PAYCHECKS...

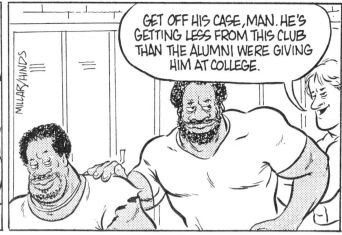

FOLKS, WE'RE HERE IN TEXAS TO COVER THIS ANNUAL MIGRATION

WELCOME TO TEXAS

THEY'RE COMING!

THEY'RE COMING!

... OF OUT-OF-STATE COACHES HOPING TO RECRUIT TEXAS HIGH SCHOOL FOOTBALL STARS...

BEECHCRAFT TWIN...

I SEE A LEAR JET

IT'S A CESSNA CITATION. SEE THE MARKINGS?

GOOD HEAVENS, IT'S A DC-3!

THE TEXAS HIGH SCHOOL FOOTBALL POOL IS HEAVILY MINED BY OUT-OF-STATE COLLEGES...

WELCOM TO TEXAS

JUST HOW MANY TEXAS SCHOOLBOYS IS ESU EYEING, COACH?

ENORMOUS STATE UNIVERSITY RECRUITING TEAM

SIX.

OIL AND CATTLE ARE TEXAS' TWO BIGGEST EXPORTS. BUT THE SURPRISING THIRD IS HIGH SCHOOL FOOTBALL PLAYERS

A SPOKESPERSON FOR THE TEXAS INDUSTRIAL DEVELOPMENT BOARD EXPLAINS...

THE EXTRA 'LAUNDRY MONEY' ALONE THESE SCHOLARSHIP BOYS SEND HOME ADDS $5.7 MILLION A YEAR TO THE STATE ECONOMY...

...WHY DO THESE BLUE-CHIP HIGH SCHOOL RUNNING BACKS HAVE TO LIVE IN THE STICKS...?

EAST TOAD STRANGLE, TEXAS POP. 534

YOU FELLERS MUST BE TRYIN' TO RECRUIT THAT WASHINGTON BOY... HIS HOUSE IS RIGHT THAT WAY.

THEY'RE A DAY LATE AND A DOLLAR SHORT...

MRS. WASHINGTON? WE'D LIKE TO TALK TO YOUR SON ABOUT PLAYING HIS COLLEGE FOOTBALL FOR THE FIGHTING SANDCRABS...

THERE'S GOTTA BE ANOTHER WAY INTO THAT HOUSE...

NOW SERVING 21

TAKE A NUMBER FOR BETTER SERVICE

YOUNG LADY, WE'RE IN A HURRY TO SEE YOUR BROTHER...

...BEFORE THAT BLUE-CHIP RUNNING BACK SIGNS TO PLAY COLLEGE FOOTBALL FOR SOMEONE BESIDES THE FIGHTING SANDCRABS...

WOULD YOU BE INTERESTED IN A SUBSTANTIAL GRANT-IN-AID FOR EXTENSIVE INFORMAL STUDY OF CONTEMPORARY CLOTHING TRENDS?

THAT $200,000 COULD HAVE BOUGHT A NEW ANTHROPOLOGY LAB...PAID FOR TWO NEW EARTH-SCIENCES PROFESSORS...

FACULTY CLUB

STATE U. PAYS $200,000 FOR COACH'S CONTRACT

IS THIS A UNIVERSITY WITH A FOOTBALL PROGRAM OR A FOOTBALL PROGRAM WITH A UNIVERSITY?

AS IF I HAD TO ASK.

MILLAR/HINDS

...SINCE YOU GAVE THE UNIVERSITY $200,000 SO IT COULD BUY UP A FOOTBALL COACH'S CONTRACT...

MILLAR/HINDS

ALUMNI CLUB

...MAYBE YOU COULD GIVE $20,000 TO ENDOW A NEW CHAIR IN CLASSICS...

THIS CLASSICS STUFF. CAN YOU BET ON IT?

OF COURSE NOT.

STATE

ALUMNI CLUB

SLAM

STUDENTS AREN'T ALLOWED IN THERE. IT'S FOR RICH BOOSTERS ONLY.

YOU HAVE TO BE ONE OF THE 100 PERSONS WHO DONATED $20,000 TO A SPECIAL ATHLETIC FUND TO GET TO SIT UP THERE.

MILLAR

GEE. TWO MILLION BUCKS. WHAT WAS THE FUND USED FOR?

TO BUILD THE 'E' CLUB.

HINDS

YOU HAVE TO DONATE $20,000 TO THE ATHLETIC FUND TO SIT UP THERE.

WOW, THOSE PEOPLE MUST REALLY LOVE FOOTBALL.

HENRY, OL' HARLEY SAYS WE'RE PLAYING TEXAS TODAY, AND I SAY WE'RE PLAYING WAKE FOREST. YOU WANNA WALK TO THE WINDOW AND CHECK?

SURE, WE'RE SITTING UP HERE IN THE WARM, RICH-ALUMNI'S CLUB AND THE STUDENTS ARE SITTING ON HARD BENCHES IN THE SNOW...

BUT THEY HAVE SOMETHING WE DON'T, HARLEY. THEY HAVE OPPORTUNITY. THEY HAVE **YOUTH**.

FAT LOT OF GOOD IT DOES THEM, HUH HARLEY?

FAT LOT, FARLEY.

TONIGHT I BEGIN A SPECIAL THREE-PART SERIES ON SPORTS AGENTS....

ON THE SPOT SPORTS

ATHLETES' AGENTS ARE COMPLETELY UNLICENSED AND UNREGULATED....

RRRRRIING.

HELLO, HIGGINS' TEXACO.

UH....HELLO, HIGGINS' SPORTS MANAGEMENT.

HUH?

HOW ETHICAL ARE ATHLETES' AGENTS?

SPECIAL REPORT
ATHLETES' AGENTS

KID, YOU'RE NOT SUPPOSED TO SIGN WITH AN AGENT UNTIL YOU'RE THROUGH WITH YOUR COLLEGE ELIGIBILITY....

SO KEEP THIS UNDER YOUR HAT....

PASS PUNT & KICK FINALS TODAY

....ARE THEY WORTH THEIR COMMISSIONS?

SPECIAL REPORT
Athletes' Agents

YEAH, I GOT 329 OTHER CLIENTS, BUT YOU'RE MY NUMBER-ONE PRIORITY, MIKE.

GEORGE, MAN.

--SURE, GEORGE... AND I'M GONNA GET YOU THE FATTEST CONTRACT IN THE HISTORY OF BASKETBALL.

FOOTBALL, MAN, FOOTBALL!

YEAH, RIGHT.... WOULD YOU WRITE THAT DOWN FOR ME?

WE BEGIN OUR SERIES ON LOCKER-ROOM EVANGELISTS...

ON THE SPOT NEWS

LOOK, I **GO** TO CHURCH. BUT TO THESE LOCKER-ROOM EVANGELISTS, YOU'RE NOT A TRUE CHRISTIAN UNLESS YOU QUOTE SCRIPTURE IN POST-GAME INTERVIEWS.

GEORGE, WHEN LIFE PUTS YOU ON WAIVERS, DON'T YOU WANT GOD TO PICK UP YOUR OPTION?

IT'S LIKE PLAYING WITH THE AYATOLLAH.

WON'T YOU JOIN THE SOCIETY OF PIOUS JOCKS...?

OKAY, FRANK, LET ME GET THIS STRAIGHT. THE SOCIETY BELIEVES THAT IF I THROW A COMPLETION...

THE LORD GUIDES YOUR HAND.

AND IF I THROW AN INCOMPLETION

THE LORD GUIDES YOUR HAND.

TO BE HONEST, FRANK, I DON'T SEE ANY PERCENTAGE...

OKAY, THE COAST'S CLEAR.

WHY DO YOU HAVE TO SNEAK TO USE THE WHIRLPOOL?

IF ONE OF THOSE LOCKER-ROOM EVANGELISTS SEES YOU GET INTO THE WATER, HE'LL TRY TO BAPTIZE YOU.

AREN'T YOU GOING TO INTERVIEW THE LOCKER-ROOM EVANGELISTS?

I AM ON EARTH TO DO THE LORD'S WILL...

Locker Room

I DIDN'T WANT TO DROP THAT PASS...

...BUT THE LORD WILLED IT.

THE LORD IS MY ALIBI. I SHALL NOT WANT.

GEORGE, THE BASHERS HAVE 27 MEMBERS OF THE SOCIETY OF PIOUS TO OUR 26. **YOU** COULD BE THE DIFFERENCE.

FRANK, DO YOU **REALLY** THINK GOD WOULD DETERMINE THE OUTCOME OF A PRO FOOTBALL GAME ON THE BASIS OF HOW MANY PLAYERS GO TO PRE-GAME PRAYER DRILLS?

THE LORD KEEPS MYSTERIOUS STATS.

FRANK, THE LORD SPOKE TO ME LAST NIGHT.

HE DID? O, PRAISE! PRAISE! DOES THIS MEAN YOU'LL JOIN THE SOCIETY OF PIOUS JOCKS?

FRANK, I'M AFRAID HE SAID THAT HE DOESN'T GIVE A DARN ABOUT PRO FOOTBALL

GEORGE, I'M AFRAID THAT YOU WERE TALKING WITH THE WRONG LORD.

WE **HAVE** TO DO SOMETHING ABOUT THESE LOCKER ROOM EVANGELISTS...

AND NOW, THE STARTING OFFENSIVE LINEUP FOR THE SMASHERS...

...STARTING AT LEFT GUARD...

TAKE A FEW MINUTES TO READ THIS...

...WON'T YOU TAKE A FEW MINUTES...

...AND NOW, INTRODUCING THE STARTING OFFENSE FOR THE BASHERS...

BOY, YOU THINK **WE** HAVE A LOT OF LOCKER-ROOM EVANGELISTS ON OUR TEAM...

HOW'D YOU LIKE TO PLAY FOR THE BASHERS?

HARE KRISNA HARE RAMA HARE KRISNA HARE RAMA...

CHING-CHINK CHING

TINGALING TINGALING TINGALING

CHINK

CHINK CHINK

THE SCHOOL IS THE SMALLEST IN THE CONFERENCE AND THE FOOTBALL TEAM USUALLY ENDS UP A DOORMAT FOR THE BIG STATE UNIVERSITIES...

...BUT THE BAND HAS BECOME NATIONALLY FAMOUS FOR ITS OUTRAGEOUS HALFTIME SHOWS...

AND HERE THEY COME NOW, MARCHING OUT ON THE FIELD AND FORMING A...A...

OH MY GOODNESS...

TANK, OUR TEAM IS USUALLY A DOORMAT FOR THE BIG STATE SCHOOLS IN THE CONFERENCE.

SO WE TRY TO MAKE THE HALFTIME SHOW COMEDY RELIEF.

OF COURSE, IT'S GETTING HARDER AND HARDER TO TOP THE FIRST HALF OF THE GAME...

THE COUNTRY'S MOST IRREVERENT AND OUTRAGEOUS COLLEGE BAND IS REHEARSING THIS WEEK'S HALFTIME SHOW...

WHAT IS THIS FORMATION?

IT'S A CAN OF SPRAY PAINT, TANK.

THE THEME IS: 'A SALUTE TO CAMPUS GRAFFITI.'

EVEN IN THE HALFTIME SHOW AT OTHER SCHOOLS, THE BAND OFTEN MAKES FUN OF THE TRADITIONS OF THE HOST COLLEGE...

IS EVERYBODY A GOOD SPORT ABOUT IT?

USUALLY, TANK... BUT JUST IN CASE, WE ALWAYS SAVE OUR RFB FORMATION FOR THE LAST.

SOMETHING YOU SPELL OUT?

NO, IT MEANS 'RUN FOR THE BUSSES.'

...IN MOST COLLEGES, THE ATHLETES ARE KEPT IN SPECIAL DORMITORIES, ARE FED IN SEPARATE PLACES...

...AS A RESULT OF THE ELABORATE SAFEGUARDS, THEY PRESENT NO DANGER TO THE GENERAL STUDENT POPULATION...

THE PRECEDING MESSAGE WAS FURNISHED BY THE NCAA.

CHUCK, YOU AND YOUR TEAMMATES PLAYED A KIND OF GAME WHERE YOU GOT POINTS FOR REALLY HARD HITS ON YOUR OPPONENTS...

RIGHT, TANK. TWO POINTS IF A GUY COULDN'T GET UP RIGHT AWAY, THREE IF HE HAD TO BE HELPED OFF THE FIELD.

AND YOUR HIT ON CHARLIE SMITH?

OH, HE WAS AT LEAST A SEVEN.

CHUCK, YOUR BOOK HAS CAUSED A TERRIBLE STINK...

WHAT I SAY IS TRUE, ISN'T IT?

YES, CHUCK, BUT...

(SIGH) HAVE YOU EVER HEARD THE PHRASE 'PUBLIC RELATIONS'?

IT'S A ROTATING DUTY. EVERY ASSOCIATE PROFESSOR DOES IT ONCE.

DO I HAVE TO SERVE?

DO YOU WANT TENURE?

ESU FACULTY STAFF

Outstanding Student-Athlete Search Committee

OKAY, WHAT ARE THE CRITERIA...?

ESU FACULTY STAFF

Outstanding Student-Athlete Search Committee

I MEAN, DOES HE HAVE TO BE ABLE TO READ THE AWARD CERTIFICATE?

DESIRABLE, BUT NOT ESSENTIAL.

HEY, LOOK AT THIS FOOTBALL PLAYER, McGRADY. HE'S GOT A 98 AVERAGE!

ESU FACULTY STAFF

Outstanding Student-Athlete Search Committee

INTERESTING...ALL EXTENSION COURSES FROM THE EASTERN NEVADA UNIVERSITY AND STORM DOOR COMPANY, INC....

OOPS, MY MISTAKE. '98' IS HIS POST OFFICE BOX NUMBER.

AFTER BOBBY WASN'T PICKED IN THE NFL DRAFT, HE SUED ESU FOR HIS POOR COLLEGE EDUCATION...

...WHICH DIDN'T PREPARE HIM TO MAKE A LIVING OUTSIDE OF FOOTBALL.

SAYS HIS ATTORNEY...

WE INTEND TO PROVE THAT THE UNIVERSITY WAS NEGLIGENT IN NOT DETERMINING THAT BOBBY HAD CEMENT HANDS...

...AND IN NOT PUTTING HIM ON A REAL-STUDENT TRACK.

THE EX-ESU TIGHT END IS SUING THE UNIVERSITY FOR FAILING TO PROVIDE HIM A MEANINGFUL EDUCATION.

BUT DOESN'T BOBBY HAVE A DEGREE?

SURE DOES. BOBBY, READ TANK YOUR DIPLOMA.

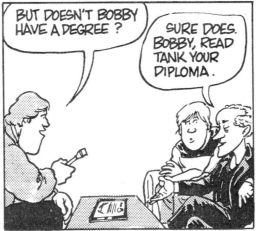

BAA...BAT ...SHEE...SHEE ...OR...

THAT'S 'BACHELOR,' BOBBY.

NEXT QUESTION?

THE ATTORNEY FOR THE EX-ESU TIGHT END IS SUING THE UNIVERSITY FOR FAILING TO PROVIDE HIM A MEANINGFUL EDUCATION.

ALL ESU WANTED WAS FOR BOBBY TO PLAY FOOTBALL. HE WAS **TOLD** TO TAKE MICKEY MOUSE COURSES.

HE HAS A DEGREE, BUT HE CAN'T READ HIS DIPLOMA!

LOOK, THIS **IS** AN INSTITUTE OF HIGHER EDUCATION.

WE EXPECT OUR STUDENTS TO BE ABLE TO READ WHEN THEY GET HERE.

AFTER NOT BEING PICKED IN THE NFL DRAFT, THE EX-TIGHT END SUED ESU FOR HIS POOR COLLEGE EDUCATION.

BUT HIS SUIT WAS DISMISSED. HIS ATTORNEY SAYS HE'LL TRY AGAIN.

COACHING MALPRACTICE. THIS KID WAS A GUARANTEED FIRST-ROUNDER UNTIL THOSE MULLETS SHIFTED HIM AWAY FROM HIS NATURAL POSITION.

...THE HOST AND OUR INSIDE-INFORMATION EXPERT ARE SLUGGING IT OUT DURING A COMMERCIAL BREAK! WHAT AM I SUPPOSED TO DO?

HE SAYS TO TAPE IT AND THEY'LL CREATE A CATEGORY FOR IT ON ONE OF THE TRASHSPORTS SHOWS...

MILLAR/HINDS

FIVE SECONDS...FOUR, THREE...

DEBBIE, YOU'LL HAVE TO DO THE SCORES!

PRO FOOTBALL UPDATE

IN THE SECOND QUARTER, IT'S GREEN BAY 14--

MILLAR/HIND

DON'T YOU **DARE** GET BLOOD ON MY OSCAR DE LA RENTA!

HONEST, RON, I DON'T SEE--

AAUUUGGH!! MY FACE!! THAT TWO-BIT GAMBLER HAS DISFIGURED ME FOR LIFE!!

STUDIO MONITOR 18

I LOOK LIKE THE **ELE**PHANT MAN!!

...JUST THANK HEAVEN YOUR HAIR IS ALL RIGHT..

YOU THINK THEY'RE GOING TO WANT THE **ELE**PHANT MAN TO HOST 'TRASHSPORTS BATTLE OF THE PRO ESCORT-SERVICE GIRLS'?!?

THAT FISTFIGHT ON THE 'PRO FOOTBALL UPDATE' SHOW BOOSTED THE RATING TWO POINTS.

IF RON AND CHARLEY JUST HADN'T BURIED THE HATCHET...

OH, CHARLEE, YOU'LL NEVER BELIEVE WHAT RON SAID ABOUT YOU TO THE 'NATIONAL ENQUIRER'...

YOU'RE POSING FOR A CENTERFOLD IN 'PLAYGIRL'?

BASHERS

BASHERS

...AFTER THEY STARTED LETTING WOMEN SPORTSWRITERS INTO THE DRESSING ROOMS, I FIGURED IT WOULDN'T BE ANY BIG DEAL....

BUCK'S DOING HIS 'PLAYGIRL' CENTERFOLD SESSION TODAY...

DECEMBER

OKAY, BUCK, HOLD THE BALL LIKE YOU'RE GOING TO PUNT IT... A LITTLE HIGHER... A LITTLE LOWER...

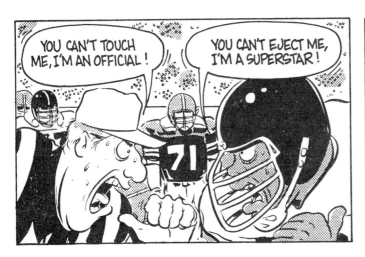

...SO WE FALSIFIED A FEW TRANSCRIPTS....BUT DO COACHES HAVE TENURE?

YEAH. WHAT IF CHEMISTRY PROFESSORS WERE EVALUATED ON THE BASIS OF WINNING OR LOSING...?

BUT—BUT—

SIGMUND, THE ALUMNI WERE REALLY COUNTING ON YOUR WINNING THE NOBEL PRIZE THIS YEAR...

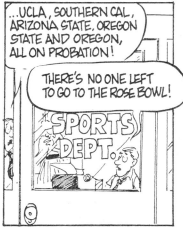

...UCLA, SOUTHERN CAL, ARIZONA STATE, OREGON STATE AND OREGON, ALL ON PROBATION!

THERE'S NO ONE LEFT TO GO TO THE ROSE BOWL!

SPORTS DEPT.

WAIT—ISN'T THERE ONE OTHER TEAM IN THE CONFERENCE?

GOOD GRIEF, YOU'RE RIGHT!... FUNNY LITTLE PLACE... STARTS WITH A 'C'...

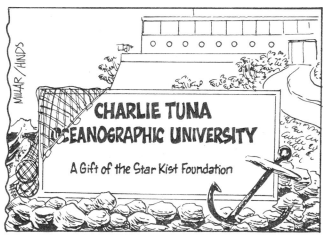

CHARLIE TUNA OCEANOGRAPHIC UNIVERSITY

A Gift of the Star Kist Foundation

YES... YES... YES...

CHARLIE TUNA OCEANOGRAPHIC UNIVERSITY Office of the President

THIS IS INTERESTING. SEEMS ALL THE OTHER SCHOOLS IN THE CONFERENCE HAVE BEEN PUT ON PROBATION. WE'RE IN THE ROSE BOWL BY DEFAULT.

YES, YES, I'M MAKING A NOTE, AND WE'LL SEE WHAT WE CAN DO. DID YOU SAY JANUARY 15TH OR JANUARY 1ST...?

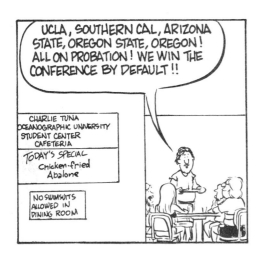

UCLA, SOUTHERN CAL, ARIZONA STATE, OREGON STATE, OREGON! ALL ON PROBATION! WE WIN THE CONFERENCE BY DEFAULT!!

CHARLIE TUNA
OCEANOGRAPHIC UNIVERSITY
STUDENT CENTER
CAFETERIA

TODAY'S SPECIAL
Chicken-fried
Abalone

NO SWIMSUITS
ALLOWED IN
DINING ROOM

WE'RE IN THE ROSE BOWL! WE'RE IN THE ROSE BOWL!

WAIT A MINUTE. WE DON'T HAVE A FOOTBALL TEAM.

MILLAR/HINDS

IF CHARLIE TUNA OCEANOGRAPHIC UNIVERSITY CAN GET A TEAM TOGETHER, WE WIN THE CONFERENCE BY DEFAULT!

MILLAR/HINDS

YOU CAN PLAY IN THE ROSE BOWL!

WHEN IS IT?

JANUARY FIRST.

CAN'T DO IT, MAN, THE HUMPBACKS WILL BE CALVING.

I KNOW BUT JUST FOR THE AFTERNOON...

WITH A ROSE BOWL INVITATION ALREADY ASSURED, THE PICK-UP FOOTBALL TEAM OF TINY CHARLIE TUNA OCEANOGRAPHIC UNIVERSITY HELD ITS FIRST MEDIA DAY...

MILLAR/HINDS

...WHAT I CAN'T UNDERSTAND IS HOW THEY CAN MAKE FUN OF FOOTBALL...

ASSISTANT COACH

COACH

I SUPPOSE IF WE'RE GOING TO COMPETE IN INTERCOLLEGIATE FOOTBALL, WE'LL NEED SOME TRADITIONS.

CHARLIE TUNA
ANOGRAPHIC UNIVERSITY
Gift of the Star Kist Foundation

LIKE CHEERLEADERS?

INEVITABLY.

CHARLIE TUNA
OCEANOGRAPHIC UNIVERSITY
Office of the President

WHERE DOES ONE FIND CHEERLEADERS?

AH HA. THE CALIFORNIA STATE HOME FOR THE OVERENTHUSIASTIC HAS A PLACEMENT SERVICE.

...AND YOU WANT US TO PROVIDE CHEERLEADERS?

NATIONAL ORGANIZATION OF WOMEN

SOMEBODY HAS TO DO IT.

WHAT IF THESE CHEERLEADERS DO SOMETHING IMPUDENT? DISRESPECTFUL OF THE BASIC IDEA OF INTERCOLLEGIATE FOOTBALL?

I'D BE TERRIBLY DISAPPOINTED IF THEY DIDN'T.

CHEERLEADERS, OF COURSE, ARE MERELY CELEBRANTS OF THE MALE FANTASY THAT WOMEN'S NATURAL PLACE IS ON LIFE'S SIDELINES, IDOLIZING THEM.

SO WE FIGURED, LET'S GO WITH IT.

POM POMS TO MATCH, I ASSUME?

IF WE'RE GOING TO PLAY IN THE ROSE BOWL, WE SHALL NEED SOME FOOTBALL TRADITIONS. I'VE DONE A LITTLE RESEARCH ON THE BIG FOOTBALL FACTORY UNIVERSITIES...

"FIGHT SONG"... "SCHOOL COLORS"... "MASCOT"...

"RECRUITING VIOLATIONS"?

THAT, APPARENTLY, IS ONE OF THE MOST HALLOWED.

FELLOWS, WE'VE FOUND OUT THAT VIOLATING RECRUITING REGULATIONS IS ONE OF THE MOST VENERABLE OF FOOTBALL TRADITIONS, SO...

PROPERTY OF CHARLIE TUNA OCEANOGRAPHIC UNIVERSITY ATHLETIC DEPT.

...BEFORE WE HAVE TO RESORT TO DRAWING LOTS, WOULD ANY OF YOU **LIKE** THE TRANS-AM...?

ARE YOU KIDDING? WITH ITS EPA MILEAGE RATING?

...ANOTHER FOOTBALL TRADITION, I'M AFRAID...

THIS IS GETTING ANNOYING, AND IN THE MIDDLE OF THE KELP MIGRATION, TOO...

BURSAR   PRESIDENT

CHARLIE TUNA UNIVERSITY RESERVED DOCKING

A COACH. EVERY SCHOOL WITH AN INTERCOLLEGIATE FOOTBALL PROGRAM HAS ONE.

BUT OUR PLAYERS AGREED TO PLAY ONLY IF THERE WEREN'T ANY PLAYS.

OH, HE DOESN'T NEED TO **COACH**, JUST TO COMMIT THE TRADITIONAL RECRUITING VIOLATIONS.

MILLAR/HINDS

THERE'S MORE TO HAVING AN INTERCOLLEGIATE FOOTBALL TEAM THAN I'D IMAGINED....

CHARLIE TUNA OCEANOGRAPHIC UNIVERSITY FACULTY LOUNGE

PUSH

I SUPPOSE I'LL HAVE TO START KEEPING UP...

MILLAR/HINDS

I'LL HAVE TO START LOOKING AT THE SPORTS SECTION.

LOOK ON THE BRIGHT SIDE. ONE FINDS LOTS OF NICE BARGAINS ON TIRES AND LIQUOR IN THE ADVERTISEMENTS..

...BUT ALL THE CAMPUS ANNOUNCEMENTS SAID IT WAS AN ANTI-DRAFT-REGISTRATION DEMONSTRATION.

MILLAR/HINDS

CHARLIE TUNA OCEANOGRAPHIC UNI

A Gift of the Sugar Kist

CTOU

PEOPLE WILL LEAVE WHEN THEY FIND IT'S A PEP RALLY.

NOT AFTER WE ROLL DOWN THE MOVIE SCREEN AND START SHOWING THE RONALD REAGAN BLOOPER REEL, THEY WON'T.

CTOU

HEY, I THINK A FOOTBALL HOMECOMING FESTIVAL WOULD BE TERRIFIC.

CHARLIE TUNA OCEANOGRAPHIC UNIVERSITY STUDENT CENTER

THERE IS A SMALL PROBLEM. THE TEAM HASN'T BEEN AWAY YET.

SURE IT HAS. IT WENT TO BIG SUR FOR THE SEA URCHIN CENSUS.

WELL OKAY, LET'S PARTY **DOWN** !

DESQUAMATION CLINIC OPENS AT 7AM

MILLAR/HINDS

...AND SINCE WE'RE ON SUSPENSION, CHARLIE TUNA UNIVERSITY WILL GO TO THE ROSE BOWL WHETHER WE WIN OR LOSE THIS GAME, AND...

...AND...AND...THERE'S REALLY NO POINT TO ANY OF THIS, IS THERE...?

...THE COACH IS IN THE UNIVERSITY CENTER HOSPITAL IN STABLE CONDITION RECOVERING FROM WHAT DOCTORS REPORTED TO BE A MODERATE EXISTENTIAL EXPERIENCE...

ON THE SPOT SPORTS

...ARIZONA STATE IS UP BY 346 POINTS, BUT SINCE ASU IS ON PROBATION, CHARLIE TUNA UNIVERSITY IS IN THE ROSE BOWL ANYWAY...

ASU COMES OUT ON OFFENSE IN THE I-FORMATION...

...AND CHARLIE TUNA COMES OUT IN THE TAI-CHI DEFENSE...

M!-A!-C!-H!-O!...

WHOOOO....NEEDS IT?

WHAT MAKES CHARLIE TUNA UNIVERSITY'S CHEERLEADING SQUAD SO UNUSUAL IS THAT THEY ARE ALL MEMBERS OF THE CAMPUS CHAPTER OF THE NATIONAL ORGANIZATION FOR WOMEN.

...A COMFORTABLE HOUSE, TWO BEAUTIFUL CHILDREN, A LOVING WIFE...

...AND FOUR BOWL GAMES IN THE SAME DAY.

LIFE IS RICH, HELEN.

LIFE IS RICH, SWEATSOX...

...TAPE-DELAY COVERAGE OF THE...

...AND THE SCORE HERE IN THE ROSE BOWL...

...HE MAKES AN INCREDIBLE CATCH...

SINCE CHARLIE TUNA WILL BE IN THE ROSE BOWL BY DEFAULT, DO YOU HAVE TROUBLE GETTING UP FOR GAMES?

USED TO, MAN...

...THEN I BOUGHT ONE OF THOSE ALARM RADIOS, YOU KNOW? MAN, NOBODY CAN SLEEP THROUGH TED NUGENT AT 100 DECIBELS...

CHARLIE TUNA OCEANOGRAPHIC UNIVERSITY GOT IN THE ROSE BOWL BECAUSE ALL OTHER SCHOOLS IN ITS CONFERENCE WERE PUT ON PROBATION.

WHAT WOULD CTOU GAIN FROM A BOWL APPEARANCE?

IT HELPS OUR RECRUITING, TANK.

WARREN HERRING CTOU PRESIDENT

BUT ISN'T CTOU GIVING UP FOOTBALL AFTER THIS GAME?

OUR PROGRAM TO RECRUIT PEOPLE TO HELP WITH THE HUMPBACK WHALE CENSUS...

...AND HERE COME MICHIGAN'S OPPONENTS, THE CHARLIE TUNA OCEANOGRAPHIC UNIVERSITY KELP...

IS THAT THE FOOTBALL TEAM, OR THE PEOPLE WHO RODE THE PARADE FLOAT...?

'...THE PRESIDENT OF CHARLIE TUNA OCEANOGRAPHIC UNIVERSITY...'

'...SAID THAT THE SCHOOL'S $400,000 ROSE BOWL SHARE...'

...$400,000 WOULD HAVE GIVEN ME THE FINEST SLUSH FUND IN THE COUNTRY...

'...WOULD BE USED TO FUND A STORY ON THE HARMFUL EFFECTS OF FOOTBALL ON AMERICAN EDUCATION...'

I CAN'T STAND IT.

....ATHLETES ARE PAMPERED.... SPORTSWRITERS GET TREATED LIKE SECOND-CLASS CITIZENS....

...THEY GET PAID MILLIONS... WHAT DO I GET? $30,000 A YEAR....

AND ALL THEY DO IS PLAY CHILDREN'S GAMES!

I CAN **TYPE!**

...THE HOTEL NEWSSTAND CLERK TOLD THIS REPORTER...THE VETERAN QUARTERBACK...

MILLAR/HINDS

...PURCHASED A PACKAGE OF CHEWING GUM... AND A COPY OF PLAYBOY...

DO YOU EVER GET THE FEELING THE SUPER BOWL IS OVERREPORTED...?

SUPER BOWL PRESS ROOM

"..AND SO, ON THE EVE OF THIS MOST FATEFUL DAY IN MAN'S HISTORY, ALL EYES LOOK TO PASADENA. AND THE WHOLE WORLD WAITS..."

COPY DESK

WORLD-BANNER-TRIBUN

GOOD LORD, IT'S JUST A **FOOTBALL** GAME.

TRY TELLING THAT TO OUR SPORTS EDITOR.

MILLAR/HINDS

...IN THE PRE-GAME INTERVIEWS, YOU'RE CASUALLY WEARING THE SUDZ® BEER CAP AND THE DOUBLE DOODLEBURGER® T-SHIRT.

THEN YOU SWITCH TO THE CIRRUS® AIRLINES CAP FOR WEARING ON THE SIDELINES.

MILLAR/HINDS

AND FOR THE POSTGAME LOCKER ROOM INTERVIEWS, YOU'RE CASUALLY WEARING THE SMOOTHIE® SHOCK ABSORBER CAP.

WHAT ABOUT THE TITANIC TACO® T-SHIRT?

THEIR CHECK BOUNCED.

HEAVENS, I'VE NEVER SEEN SWEATSOX SO DEPRESSED.

HE LOST HIS BET ON THE SUPER BOWL.

GOOD LORD, WHAT DID HE BET? HIS HOUSE? ALL HIS SAVINGS?

THAT IF HE LOST, HE COULDN'T WATCH THE PRO BOWL ON TV.

SWEATSOX LOST HIS SUPER BOWL BET?

YEP. HE CAN'T WATCH THE PRO BOWL GAME ON TV.

THAT'S A HEAVY BET. WHAT SORT OF BOOKIE GIVES ACTION LIKE THAT?

HIS WIFE.

...SWEATSOX'S TEAM LOST, SO I WON THE BET. HE CAN'T WATCH THE PRO BOWL GAME, WHATEVER **THAT** IS, ON TV.

AND IF **YOUR** TEAM HAD LOST THE SUPER BOWL...?

I'D HAVE HAD TO WATCH THE PRO BOWL GAME WITH HIM.

HELEN!!

I SWEATED THE WHOLE SECOND HALF.

YOU BET ON THE SUPER BOWL WITH SWEATSOX...

... AND HE LOST.

'I WILL NOT WATCH THE PRO BOWL GAME ON TV.'

HOLDING HIS MARKER, HUH?

BUT SWEATSOX, IT'S ONLY YOUR **WIFE**!!

.... IT'S NOT LIKE IT'S A **BOOKIE**, SWEATSOX!

THINK, SWEATSOX, THINK! IT'S THE LAST PRO FOOTBALL GAME UNTIL SEPTEMBER!

A MAN'S MARKER IS A MAN'S MARKER.

...PRO BOWL GAME'S STARTING, AND I CAN'T WATCH IT...

I KNOW YOU LOST OUR BET, AND YOU GIVE UP WATCHING THE GAME...

...BUT I'M WILLING TO TEAR UP YOUR MARKER...

HOW MUCH?

TWO KISSES.

I'LL PAY THE OTHER ONE AFTER THE GAME.

SMAK!

CLICK! ...AND NOW, THE SEASON PREMIERE OF NFL MONDAY NIGHT FOOTBALL!

YOU KNOW, LIFE REALLY **IS** WORTH LIVING...